kingfisher

kingfisher

Paolo Fioratti

TRANSLATED BY SYLVIA SULLIVAN

HarperCollins*Publishers*

Dedico questo libro ai miei genitori
I dedicate this book to my parents

HarperCollinsPublishers
London Glasgow Sydney Auckland
Toronto Johannesburg

© 1992 Paolo Fioratti
English translation © 1992 HarperCollinsPublishers

ISBN 0 00 219957 2

Printed and bound in England by The Bath Press

CONTENTS

Malachite kingfisher (Corythornis
cristata) *perched on a papyrus
along the banks of the river
Okawango in Botswana*

INTRODUCTION

*i**n the countryside of Veneto, not far from Venice, the fronds of an old willow drooped over a stand of hawthorns, towards the water of a channel. On a branch in the shade, a little bird of turquoise-blue perched immobile, watching the water surface in search of prey. The colour of its plumage was very vibrant, but the kingfisher blended in so well with its environment it would have been difficult to discern it had I not known that was its usual perch. Suddenly, it displayed a degree of alarm, thrusting its bill skywards, due to the voices of local labourers who were carrying out the winter pruning in a nearby vineyard. It was more disturbed, however, by the presence of another kingfisher, in the face of which it had once more to impose its own territorial dominance.*

These observations arise from the time when, as a boy, I tried to photograph the kingfisher, concealing myself amongst the vegetation along the riverbanks. My limited equipment consisted of an old telemetric camera, and naturally I had difficulty in obtaining pictures from fleeting views.

At that time, not only my apparatus, but also my knowledge of natural history was very limited and, perhaps because of this, the aspect that I found most interesting did not concern physiology or ethology, but evolution; the origins of the kingfisher, which to me appeared so remote compared with other species present in the same places. I believed that its dispersal in search of new regions probably happened during the geological and climatic upheavals of the past, and considered that even today it does not find it easy to survive. The changes in the countryside, the canalisation and pollution of water courses, the lowering of water tables, and the cutting of river vegetation often prevent it from colonising new areas.

I realised, nevertheless, that my interpretations were rather empirical and superficial, owing more to imagination than objective consideration of the events. So I began to investigate more deeply and to consider the camera as an irreplaceable means of documentation. In fact, before this instrument existed, it fell to zoologists to furnish descriptions that were not subjective. This was fundamentally (and in part is still today) the dilemma of ethology as a science: the fact that it is not always possible to reproduce observations made in the field and therefore their accuracy is not guaranteed.

Although I did not want to pretend to describe in photographs the entire life of a species with so complex and interesting a biology, I proposed, however, at least to document the most significant aspects. And, because it was also my intention to utilise the photographic equipment in the most objective way possible, I decided to take all my photos under perfectly natural conditions. That means that I did not have recourse to tanks, small basins or any artificial reconstruction of the environment, but that I photographed the kingfisher in its own natural habitat. The results are the pictures in this book.

ORIGINS

*t*he sun begins to dissolve the mist and vapours of the winter morning, and the willow, illuminated by wavering light, is reflected in the calm water of the canal. In splendid livery, the kingfisher loudly announces its presence. Its brilliant colour changes with the angle of the light, passing from emerald-green to turquoise-blue. The short, coral-red legs, the compact shape of the body, the remarkable proportions of the head and bill, testify that the kingfisher appears to originate from an environment richer in form, colour and variety of creatures than our own. Moreover, of the few tropical species which in past epochs have become established in what is known as the Old World (the hoopoe, bee-eater, roller, golden oriole and perhaps the swift), it is the only one which has become resident and has ceased to migrate.

The hypothesis that selection for continuous residency should be determined by the availability of food seems plausible: fish, in contrast to insects, can be abundant in winter. Moreover, competition with similar, very territorial species which are resident in the places of origin might have discouraged return migration. Evidently, there were also other ecological factors which, with our current methods of investigation, we are not able to identify precisely but about which we can only theorise. In fact the ancient and, at the same time, rapid evolutionary history of birds makes it practically impossible to date with certainty the periods of differentiation and spread of the various species of the world. The fact that current distribution is the result of rather recent geological phenomena simplifies matters.

What concerns us is reconstructing recent history (let us say from the end of the Tertiary), forgetting more remote events that are untraceable. Even if palaeontological evidence is not very plentiful, it is usually possible to establish that the geographical distribution of birds in past ages was different from that now. In the Tertiary, many tropical species were present in western Europe, a testimony to the existence of a climate very different from today's. In the Quaternary, the great climatic swings and the glaciations which followed were in their turn responsible for the last modifications to bird distribution. These variations continue to happen today, albeit to a different extent, because of man's influences on the

The European kingfisher (Alcedo atthis) *in its natural habitat*

environment. This is why biogeography is essentially the study of a dynamic phenomenon that is in continuous evolution. Glancing at a map of the world, we can also see how the history of diversification and dispersal is linked to the history of evolution of the emergent landmasses. The northern hemisphere is made up of a continental mass that is much more homogeneously distributed than the southern hemisphere, and this explains the greater homogeneity of the species which live in this region of the earth. They have been able to spread quickly because of the absence of natural barriers. By contrast, the existence of oceanic basins in the southern hemisphere has impeded rapid diffusion and favoured differentiation, such as diversification of species. For these reasons, the avifaunas of New Guinea, New Zealand, South America and Australia are rich and varied, numbering, between them, most of the species of kingfisher. Altogether, 49 of the 86 species of the family are resident in the region of Malaysia. This is of much interest because, as we shall see, it directly concerns our European kingfisher *(Alcedo atthis)* and its story.

Malaysia is the region comprising Indochina, the Bismarck Archipelago, and the Coral Sea, and has remained more or less stable during the course of geological eras. Within the rainforests, maintained intact and isolated up until today, there are numerous species of kingfisher – 57 per cent of all those present in the world. Many of these could be termed "primitive"; their diet and method of hunting are not highly specialised. Moreover, zoologists are concerned with the oligotypical entity, that is the genera are few in species and the species few in subspecies. Given this consideration and certain others, they admit, even without the confirmation of any remaining fossils, that it is unlikely that the central origin of speciation could be situated outside the region of Malaysia.

Those who venture into the forests of New Guinea, the Philippines or Borneo, where the water flows slowly under the curtain of vegetation or between the mangroves whose submerged roots lie in the narrow creeks of the coast, will find there four primitive representatives of the genus *Alcedo*. They constitute the original nucleus that has given birth to seven species which spread out towards Africa, Asia and Europe. *Alcedo atthis* is one of them. This last species has had a notable success in the colonisation of the Old World and is now resident in that vast area shown on the map opposite (top), known as the Western Palearctic. Our friend is so well established that it no longer returns to its place of origin. As I have said, at the root of this behaviour there are certainly reasons which are unknown to us. However, if the bird were to have retraced its steps, it would have encountered strong competition from other species: the azure kingfisher *(Alcedo azurea)* of New Guinea, for example, or the deep blue kingfisher *(A. meninting)* and blue-bearded kingfisher *(A. euryzona)* of Borneo, which are very similar to *A. atthis* in feeding habits and behaviour.

The area of distribution of Alcedo atthis. *Almost certainly originating from Malaysia, it has succeeded in establishing itself throughout this vast area. This small bird has overcome the ecological and geographical barriers that separate the tropical regions from the temperate and cold regions of the Palearctic*

The distribution of the family Alcedinidae (kingfishers) throughout the world. There are 86 species in 14 genera, including Alcedo, Ceyx *and* Corythornis

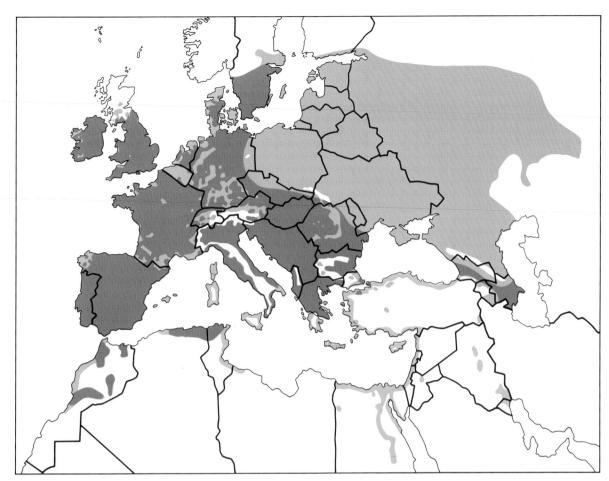

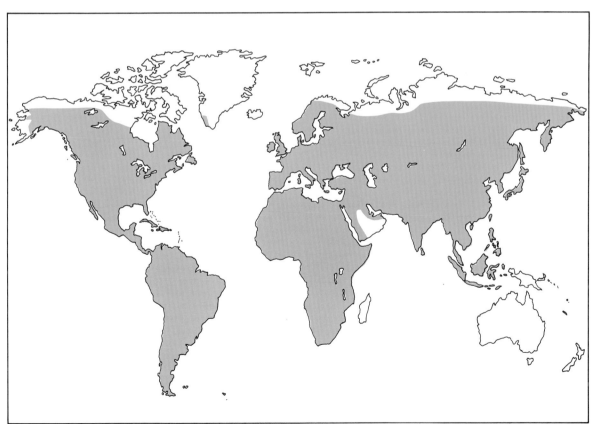

Two African species.
Below: the malachite kingfisher
(Corythornis cristata)

Right: the pied kingfisher
(Ceryle rudis)

Of the 86 species of kingfisher that exist today, an in-depth comparative and evaluative analysis has still to be made. This apparent disinterest of ornithologists in one of the most beautiful and interesting bird families is justified by the difficulty of research in the original habitats. Do not forget that the majority of kingfishers live in rainforests that are still in part unexplored, and that the habits of each species are very different.

There are nocturnal species like the hook-billed kingfisher (*Melidora macrorrhina*), and others like the shovel-billed kingfisher (*Clytoceyx rex*) which ascends to some 2500m in the mountainous forests of New Guinea. The smallest species is the African dwarf kingfisher, a tiny forest-dwelling bird that weighs about 8g. Others are massive, like the kookaburra (*Dacelo gigas*), an Australian species which weighs as much as 500g. As is easy to imagine, their feeding regimes are also diverse and often determined by anatomical characteristics. In addition, not all the species are associated with aquatic environments like *Alcedo atthis*. On the contrary, the most numerous group, comprising 66 species, is typically confined to terrestrial or, to a minor extent, semi-aquatic habitats. Examples are the Daceloninae, and the genera *Ceyx* and *Corythornis* of the Alcedininae which feed on invertebrates and small vertebrates caught on the ground or by inserting the bill into the soil.

The remaining 20 species, 11 *Alcedo* and 9 *Cerylinae*, are totally dependent on aquatic environments and only in some cases is a very modest proportion of the prey caught on the ground or in flight. There is, however, a common trait to all 86 members of the family: these hunters do not run after or pursue their prey, but strike suddenly. This characteristic is particularly obvious and spectacular in the divers, of which one of the supreme examples is the European kingfisher.

This brief journey into the history of the origins of the kingfisher cannot fail to be of interest to the study of a species which has so successfully overcome the ecological and geographical barriers that separate the animals of the tropical regions from those of the temperate and cold habitats of the Palearctic.

*White-throated or
Smyrna kingfisher
(Halcyon smyrnensis) at
Bharatpur in India*

DISTRIBUTION &

GEOGRAPHICAL

VARIATIONS

*b*efore describing in great detail the geographical distribution of *Alcedo atthis*, it is necessary to explain that this is not a static situation, but that, in time, the area changes, due to a variety of causes. Human impact, for example, has a notable influence in modifying populations and can even completely eradicate the kingfisher's presence in certain places. Having said this, today the species is widely distributed, from the British Isles and the Atlantic coast of Europe and Morocco (with the exclusion of the steppe deserts of central and south-eastern Asia and the mountains towards the east as far as Sakhalin), to the Kuril Isles, Japan and the islands of Ryukyu.

The northerly confines of the area extend from the region south of the Baltic Sea up to the southern Urals (the bird has been recorded as far north as 60° latitude, in the Siberian plateaux of Tschera-Olekma). The southerly limit stretches from Maghreb, and proceeds towards the east, from the central-eastern Mediterranean, including Sicily, Greece, Iran, Iraq, both eastern and western India (excluding the southern area of the Malacca peninsula), the continental region of south-east Asia, Sri Lanka and Taiwan. In this vast area, only slight geographical variations in the kingfisher's dimensions and colouration have been recorded and it is possible to define more or less arbitrarily the relative areas for each subspecies. The nominate species *Alcedo a. atthis* is found in the Mediterranean area as far as Maghreb, from the western part of Asia to the north-west of India, from the former Soviet Union (with the exclusion of the Baltic states and the area of St Petersburg), to lake Baikal. We can then distinguish a subspecies, *Alcedo a. ispida*, which is slightly bigger and has slightly deeper colours, a thicker bill and a darker upper mandible. It lives in the north-eastern part of the range. Finally, there are two other

A kingfisher, immobile on its perch, waiting for prey. The places where this species lives often succumb to environmental changes, especially those brought about by human interference

subspecies, which live outside these limits and differ very little from the nominate species: *Alcedo a. bengalensis* and *Alcedo a. taprobana*. The first, slightly smaller and with slightly bluer upperparts, is found from northern India to eastern Asia, to the north as far as lake Baikal, Sakhalin and Japan. The second is confined to southern India and to Ceylon. In conclusion, there remain another three or four subspecies, resident in Celebes and the tiny islands of eastern Sonda.

The 11 species of the genus Alcedo, *of which the European kingfisher is one, are distributed throughout Malaysia as well as in Australasia, tropical Africa and the Palearctic. They are (clockwise from top left):* Alcedo atthis, A. hercules, A. cyanopecta, A. caerulescens, A. pusilla, A. euryzona *(female),* A. websteri, A. azurea, A. meninting, A. quadribrachys *and* A. semitorquata

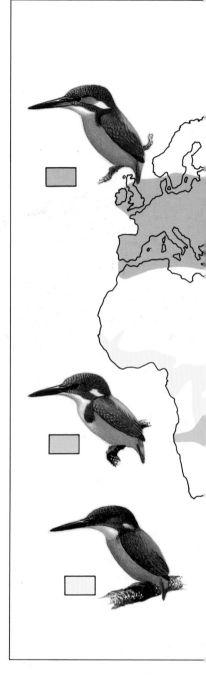

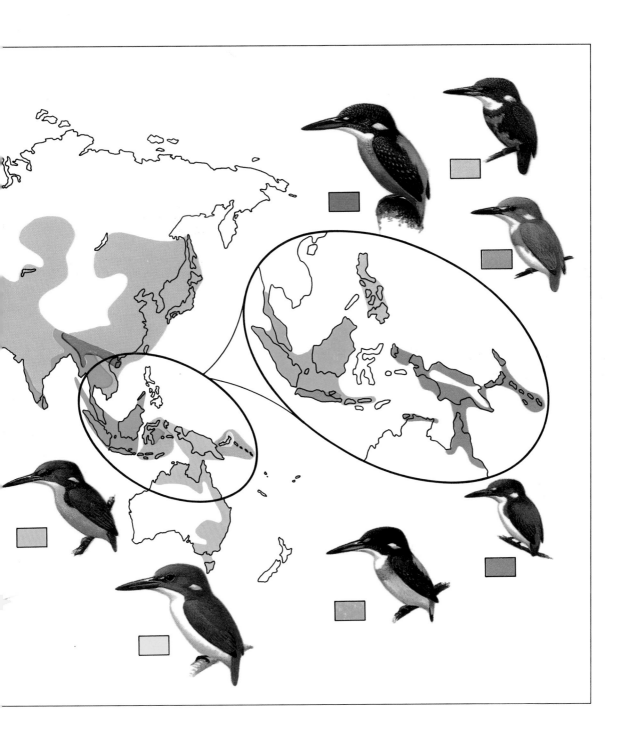

DESCRIPTION

*t*he first time anyone sees a kingfisher in flight, they will be struck more than anything by the brilliant blue colour of the bird's upperparts. In fact, one usually sees a back view as it streaks away, skimming over the water's surface. The kingfisher is a small bird, robust and compact, with a long and strong bill, large head and a very short tail, tapering towards the end. Considering all this, it is almost impossible to confuse the kingfisher with any other mid-European species.

In the male, the bill is completely black, although a patch of rosy-orange may be present on the lower mandible, whereas in the female this mark is more pronounced and covers the mandible for a proportion varying from a third to five-sixths of its total length.

The upperparts vary from cobalt blue to turquoise, the underparts are orange. Seen at close range, however, the plumage is very rich in shades and the colours change according to the angle of the light, by diffraction, of which I shall speak in a forthcoming chapter. The gradations and tones, because they are so changeable, cannot be described in an unequivocal and definitive way.

The forehead, crown and nape are dark blue-green and each feather has a pale blue patch just before the tip. The upper lores are dark chestnut, terminating in two roundish, lighter spots just before the eyes. These are bordered by two black lines which also extend to the eyes. The ear coverts are orange, like the underparts (the belly is slightly lighter) with the exception of a creamy-white patch at the throat and chin. The ear coverts are delineated, at the base, by two moustaches of turquoise and green, and behind these are two creamy-white patches that run towards the nape. From this part a beautiful stripe of brilliant cobalt runs along the centre of the back and rump to the tail. In the flanks and the remaining area of the back the kingfisher has iridescent colours, similar to those of the head and neck, with tips of pale blue on the wing coverts. The legs and feet are coral-red. The feet are unusual in that the second and third toes are joined as far as the second joint. The irides are brown. While the main differences between the two sexes concern the bill, the male has slightly more vivid colours, distinguishable only by an expert eye. The juveniles differ in that the bill is completely black, with a little white at the

A profile of the kingfisher shows how it should be impossible to confuse this bird with any other middle European species. It is a small bird - about 16-17cm in length and 39-44 g in weight

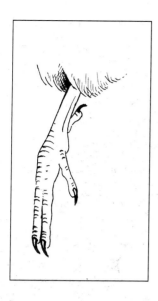

Kingfisher feet are unusual in that the second and third toes are joined as far as the second joint

tip, the feet and legs are darker, the breast feathers slightly paler and the head feathers somewhat greener.

In order to have an idea of the dimensions of the kingfisher, here are some average measurements from various regions of Europe. The wing is 76-81mm in males and females. The tail measures 35-39mm in males, and 34-40mm in females. The bill undergoes variations between the sexes, becoming shorter in summer due to abrasion caused by excavating the nest tunnel. The average length is 40-47mm for males, and 40-46mm for females. The tarsus is 9.4-10.9mm long in males, and 9.6-11.2mm in females. The feet measure 16-18mm in males, 16-19mm in females.

The weight of the kingfisher varies slightly according to subspecies and is greatest in *Alcedo a. ispida.* There are, however, seasonal variations giving different measurements in males and females. The weight of the male, for example, decreases from February/March to September, before gradually increasing until December. Without going into too much detail about the different measurements recorded in various countries, it can be stated with reasonable accuracy that the average weight of a male *Alcedo a. ispida* varies between 39 and 44g. This range has a clear enough significance, considering that the weight begins to decline during the period of courtship, throughout which the males, instead of feeding themselves, offer fish to the females, which are consuming more energy than normal. The weight continues to decrease until the breeding period has finished, before beginning to increase again.

For the above reasons and also because of the weight increase due to eggs, the female's weight varies within a range that is, in a sense, the opposite of the male's. In practice, the females put on weight from January/February to May/June, arriving at a point where they exceed the maximum weights attained by the males, before losing weight again. So, in the period of autumn dispersal and of the winter migration, the males are slightly heavier than their mates and this slight physical superiority probably explains the fact that they more easily succeed in maintaining the breeding territory, forcing the females to disperse. Before concluding, I would like to record that the reported values are averages and one should not therefore be surprised if in certain regions one encounters slight variations. In Switzerland, for example, a series of measurements from several adult birds registered values between 35 and 55g.

The silhouette of the pied kingfisher, an African species, is easily distinguishable from that of Alcedo atthis

A bleak near the surface about to be captured by a kingfisher. Sometimes the splash of the dive can be heard at a distance of several metres

Note the nictitating membrane, an additional eyelid that protects the eyes while underwater and in other circumstances

HABITAT

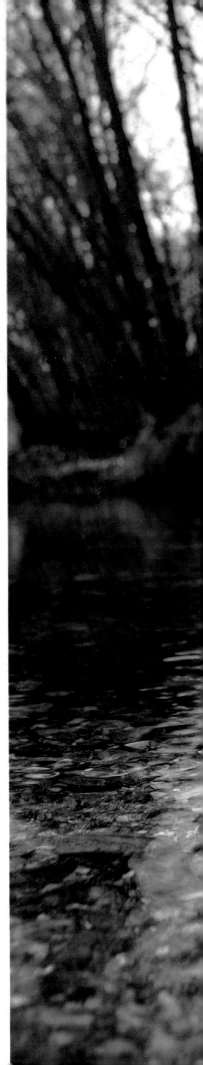

for the kingfisher, the choice of habitat within its area of distribution is determined by various elements largely independent of geographical position, latitude and climate. The first element is without doubt water, which must be clear, calm or with a weak current. The second is the availability of small fish and other suitable aquatic prey. Naturally, the water surface must be free of ice and it is also essential that there should be sufficient low perches, preferably at a height of less than two metres: emergent roots, overhanging branches, or old dry trees at the water's edge serve this purpose. The perches are used as observation posts, then as springboards from which to launch dives and they are usually positioned in shade, or in a somewhat secluded position. Dry branches, or those without too many leaves, which would make it difficult to spot prey, are almost always preferred.

Usually, small streams, ponds, canals, pits, sometimes abandoned gravel workings where the water is clear and not too deep, are preferred to large open waters such as lakes, estuaries and reservoirs. Nevertheless, the kingfisher can live along the banks of large, fast-running rivers, but in such cases, the areas selected are those where the water runs more slowly and where the shoreline is staggered, with pools, inlets and bays. Along some rivers in North Italy, like the Piave, the Sesia or the Ticino, for example, I have noted that preference is governed by contiguous pools of water, suitability for diving and the food resources of the river, more than the main river course. These habitats are always rich in vegetation and it is unlikely that the kingfisher would choose open territories or canalised water courses without trees and bushes, even if sometimes it is forced to frequent such places in the absence of more suitable habitats. It is also very improbable that it would establish itself higher than 650m

The kingfisher uses an oblique
trajectory only to capture prey
that is near the surface

above sea level even though there have been two instances of breeding higher than 900m, in Germany and Switzerland, at 910 and 990m respectively. Outside the breeding season, however, the kingfisher enlarges its habitat, extending as far as the seacoast, to islands, reservoirs and larger water bodies.

Even though the kingfisher is cautious and diffident, it can adapt to human presence and comes to fish at fish-farms. This habit could represent a significant cause of mortality, because, at least in Italy so far as I have been able to ascertain, unscrupulous farmers kill large numbers of birds with nets, shotguns or by other means. As an illustration of its capacity to adapt to human environments, I remember an amusing case some years ago. During a cold winter, a kingfisher took possession of a spraying fountain inside a private garden. The owner enjoyed fishing, and he always kept a good number of bleak in the fountain to use as bait for pike. The fountain of water kept the water surface free of ice and the bird fished there for several days until the weather became milder.

In the breeding season, another important element determines where the bird will take up residence and that is the availability of vertical banks which are suitable for excavating nesting tunnels. The preferred banks, sandy or clayey, are usually right above the water surface and without too many stones, roots or other obstructions that make it difficult to dig. However, when suitable banks are not available nearby, the kingfisher will choose other sites, even if they are a certain distance inland, as we shall see in the chapter on nesting behaviour.

The ideal environment for the kingfisher possesses several features, the most important of which are unpolluted water and the availability of small fish

Pages 32-41. The territory of the kingfisher is often frequented by other species that, except for rats, weasels and foxes, do not represent a danger for the little bird

Overleaf: a grey heron

Left: a typical bank of sand and clay where it is possible to excavate the nesting tunnel. This is an important element that characterises the habitat of the kingfisher

Above: a kingfisher scrutinises the water surface

A coot gains speed before
launching itself in flight

Overleaf: a mallard duck takes off
vertically from the water

*Below: ferns often grow in the
humid placed frequented by the
kingfisher*

*Right: a squacco heron brooding
in its nest a few metres above the
water surface*

Right: a little egret in breeding plumage

MOVEMENTS

*i*n the territory where I took my first photographs, some 30 km from Venice, the environmental conditions were ideal for kingfishers. About 15 years ago, this area held a large surface-area of water, on average little more than a metre deep, and a network of streams and channels formed a boundary to agricultural land. These watercourses made natural lines of demarcation, covered by dense vegetation along the banks. The hedges formed a sometimes impenetrable belt of brambles, hazel, alder, hornbeam, elder, whitebeam, willow and other shrubs and trees to create a veritable curtain above the water surface. Wearing boots, I was able to walk for some kilometres under this natural arc of vegetation, coming out into the open in some water tracts. This area, which was very pebbly, was the old bed of the River Piave. The water flowed particularly clearly and among the most common fish were sticklebacks, rudd, dace and bleak. For the kingfisher, this system of overgrown canals must have represented a habitat similar to its original one, where the water courses opened up a passageway into the forest. Moreover, the water current never iced over even in the coldest winters and therefore, given that there were springs, it kept an almost constant temperature. The kingfishers, strictly territorial, divided this habitat between each other, abandoning their patches only during the breeding season. Then they moved towards the streams where the vertical banks were best suited to the excavation of a nest inaccessible to predators. Each year, there were many skirmishes immediately after the breeding season. The juveniles dispersed along the water courses, invading the territories of the adults which systematically drove them out towards unoccupied areas.

The dispersal of juveniles occurs in all directions, but the longest journeys are generally towards the south and south-west. Moreover, these

Dispersal flights are principally directed towards the western and southern zones of the breeding area

movements, which sometimes extend to a remarkable distance, are more pronounced during the period from July to October, when they overlap gradually with the autumn migration of the adults.

From studies made in Czechoslovakia on a number of ringed birds, it was established that the longest journeys occurred in the direction of Yugoslavia, Italy, including Sicily, towards France, especially the south, towards south-western Spain and Malta. The maximum distance recorded was 1820km, to Alicante in southern Spain, while of those recovered, it appeared that only two adults moved further than 200 km, with distances of 610 and 790km, to Italy. Some interesting data on the length of a daily journey concerned a juvenile ringed in Holland; it travelled along the water courses, covering between seven and 30km each day, while a fledgling ringed in Ryazan, in the former Soviet Union, was recovered a month after leaving the nest, 170km distant in the direction of north north-west, confirming the hazards of dispersal. Other studies of the dispersal of juveniles have been made in various countries of western Europe and the results are analogous. For example, out of 83 nestlings ringed in Holland, of those recovered 14 had travelled further than 100km, and the longest journey of 890km was in the direction of France. Similarly, birds ringed in Belgium have provided data for recoveries in England, France and northern Spain, with a longest journey of 1100km. In particular, migrants can be forced further afield in response to a period of intense cold, and this is evidence of the great adaptability of the species, which is not constrained by conditions in its original forest habitat, where the climate is subject to much smaller variations.

The general model for dispersal was confirmed by 85 official recoveries of birds ringed in Germany, either as nestlings, juveniles or adults. The model also confirmed that the most active period of dispersal occurs in summer, when the newly-independent juveniles leave the territory occupied by their parents. Moreover, it endorsed that the adults move less than the juveniles, which is understandable as the more expert and competitive birds are more likely to succeed in establishing their own territories.

A curious fact, confirmed by many observations, is that of the adults, the females are more inclined to move away than the males. This strange phenomenon is without obvious significance, and has so far eluded researchers, because in effect every instinct of an animal in the wild has evolved to enable it to survive. Without compromising my reputation in this field, given that I am a physicist and not an ethologist, I would hazard the theory, after a good number of observations, that the males are more aggressive than the females, at least outside the breeding season. The females would therefore be forced to disperse and how such behaviour can be of use to the sexes will be discussed later on.

As I said earlier, the dispersal of juveniles in the months from July to October gradually overlaps with the autumn migration of the adults. The adults appear to be more disciplined, in the sense that they disperse in a more precise direction. In practice, the population of the kingfisher in the Western Palearctic can be subdivided into three categories, in relation to the migratory movements. The races that occupy the central and northern areas of the former Soviet Union, from the west of the range to the top of Finland and Poland, where the water freezes in winter, are demonstrably largely migratory. The populations of central Europe are instead only partially so, in response to particularly severe winters, while those of the Mediterranean basin or of the maritime regions of the west are essentially sedentary, or subject to simple movements. The autumn and winter migrations are directed towards the western and southern zones of the breeding area (although a small number take a different route), towards the Mediterranean, North Africa, including Libya and Egypt, the Gulf of Aqaba, the Red Sea, Persian Gulf, the coast of Arabia and the mangrove coasts of Pakistan and the north-west of India. Those kingfishers that reach the Middle East in winter probably come from the former Soviet Union, although this has not been proven by ringing.

The populations of eastern Siberia and northern China migrate to the south, wintering in the Philippines and Indonesia across southern Asia, overlapping with the resident populations. The kingfisher is a rare visitor to tropical Africa between March and October, from the extreme north of the Sudan. The data recorded from adult populations in Europe and Great Britain confirmed that they do not move as far away from the breeding territory as the juveniles. In England, out of 406 adults ringed, 60% travelled less than 10km from the breeding territory; 34.5% from 10 to 100km, while only 5.5% flew farther, including four birds recovered during July and August in France, Belgium and islands of Manica.

Of the kingfishers of the Western Palearctic that are subject to dispersal, migratory birds start their return journey in February. In western Europe, the breeding areas become reoccupied during the months of February or March, while populations from the former Soviet Union return there at the end of April or in May. Having returned, the birds usually nest quite close to the site occupied the previous year.

POPULATION &

MORTALITY

*e*ven though there are no recent and precise data on kingfisher populations in the various regions of its range, it is generally accepted that in central-northern European countries the species is declining. The mortality that occurs during severe winters is compensated by a remarkable reproductive capacity, enabling places to be recolonised. There have always been such natural fluctuations, but today human impact presents a new element. Water pollution, for example, besides influencing the survival of fish, the kingfisher's main food, also directly damages the bird's plumage, rendering it less able to fulfil the precise functions for which it is designed. Habitat changes, and, in particular, the artificial canalisation of many water courses, have contributed to the disappearance of natural banks suitable for nesting (usually the preferred height is between 1.5 m and 3 m). The conditions necessary for the survival of the kingfisher have been lost from many places.

If we look farther afield, we can see that from the end of the last century, the kingfisher showed an increase in population numbers, starting with Sweden in the south and gradually expanding towards the north. This expansion, however, did not last very long and from the beginning of this century, *Alcedo a. ispida* began a decline that in many parts of its range has become particularly noticeable since the middle of the 1900s. However, data do not exist on the fate of the population of *Alcedo a. a.* in more southern and eastern areas, other than recently in Italy (where there are no precedents for comparison). It is expected that in these regions too, industrialisation and habitat manipulation will have made life more difficult for the kingfisher. Because of the pressures on it, the kingfisher is on Annex I of the EC Birds Directive 1979, which means that it is among those species that "shall be the subject of special measures

A kingfisher wounded in the leg by a hunter does not have much chance of survival

concerning their habitat in order to ensure their survival and reproduction in their area of distribution".

On the whole, the species has never been very numerous and anyone who has ever wondered approximately how many pairs of kingfishers exist in various countries would probably be surprised at the low numbers. In fact, these birds have a high mortality even in places where human impact is not yet determined. If we compare kingfishers to the perfect fishing machine, we can also say that their mechanisms, so perfected, can become jammed due to a variety of causes, cold being certainly one of the most important. Above all, as long as the causes of mortality are natural ones, there is a balance between losses and recruitment. Before pursuing the argument, here are approximate numbers of resident pairs in some countries of the range in which censuses have been taken.

ITALY: there are recent data, obtained from research from the "Atlantic Project". There were in the region of 5000 to 10,000 censused pairs, and kingfishers were found nesting in localities inside Sicily and Sardinia, near freshwater courses, from 1984 to 1989. Although there are no earlier data for comparison, it appears that the species is in decline as a result of pollution and artificial modification of riverbanks.

FRANCE: the species is in decline because of disturbance by man, pollution and changes to water courses. The population would seem to be in the region of 1000-10,000 pairs, with notable variations due to cold winters.

GREAT BRITAIN AND IRELAND: In 1976 there was a population of between 5000 and 9000 pairs and one can only conclude that the species is in decline, even if one takes into account great fluctuations due to cold winters. In the United Kingdom, the kingfisher is given special protection under Schedule I of the Wildlife and Countryside Act 1981.

BELGIUM: 450 pairs. There is a decline in the south, while in the north the population appears more stable. The most important breeding areas are shown to be in the Ardenne, to the south of Sambre and Meuse, west of Ostflandern, Dyletal and to the north and south of Limburg.

LUXEMBOURG: from 1985, when 65-90 pairs were censused, there has a been a definite fall, due to water pollution. The kingfisher is present in the north (Osling) because water quality is better, while in the south it has almost disappeared.

HOLLAND: the numbers of pairs are subject to very marked

fluctuations because of hard winters. In 1975, for example, there were 275-350 pairs, while in 1976, after a very cold winter, there were 90-140.

GERMANY: there are no data on the total population, but of those partially related to various localities, one can estimate some 1000-1200 pairs in western Germany and about 250 in eastern Germany where the population is in decline due to pollution. The research carried out in 1977 showed that the population was more consistent in Bavaria (250-300 pairs) and in Westphalia (270-320 pairs).

SWITZERLAND: between 1977 and 1978, 200 pairs were censused.

SWEDEN AND DENMARK: between the two countries some 100-200 pairs were present, with marked fluctuations caused by severe winters.

FINLAND: only 10 pairs were indicated in 1958.

From this, one can understand how the total number of *Alcedo atthis* in the Palearctic could be so small. In fact, resident pairs in the different countries vary from a few to a maximum of 10,000, and to be able to understand the reasons for this situation a little better, it is necessary to examine more deeply the causes of mortality and reproductive success. Various observations made in Europe suggest that during a single breeding season a pair will rear between five and eight young to fledging. This is borne out by studies made during the years 1970 and 1980 in Switzerland, Germany, England, etc, which arrived at the same average conclusion. It would be interesting to have more recent data in order to ascertain the adverse effects of human impact since then.

As regards mortality, cold winters are a known factor in the countries of central-northern Europe, and of the adults which occupy sites near the nesting grounds, a high number succumb. In order to find out what is the lowest temperature tolerated by a kingfisher population, a study was made over nine years, on an area of about 1120 km², in north-western Germany. All the vertical walls suitable for nesting were monitored and several new ones were created.

It was thus established that kingfishers can withstand a daily temperature of about -2°C, while the situation changes when temperature drops below -5°C. In practice, a precise correlation was established between the decline of the population, temperature and the number of days during which it remained below a certain value.

Naturally, cold is not the only cause of mortality, as has been shown from various studies. In England, from 222 ringed birds, about 76% did not survive beyond the first year. However, in Holland, Austria and Germany, mortality during the first year of life is about 80%, 15% during

*Cold winters are an
important cause of mortality,
particularly when water
bodies are frozen over*

the second and 4% in the third. From these studies some interesting information on causes of mortality has been obtained. It has been discovered that 13% suffered collisions with windows or other objects, another 13% were killed directly by man, some 6% were killed by cars and only 2% preyed upon by other animals. For the remaining percentage, it is not possible to establish the precise causes of death.

As I have already said, the kingfisher compensates for high mortality with good reproductive success, the average number of nestlings which fledge for each pair being between five and eight, and it is not worth going into much further detail. Let me say only that the average number of young fledged is lowest in the most northerly countries like the former Soviet Union and is probably greatest in the southernmost regions of the range.

By contrast, it is interesting to record the result of a study at Taubergiessen, in Baden, between 1977 and 1978. The study, which directly concerned the success or failure of nest construction, revealed that 72% of nest tunnels were completed, 20% were flooded after the water level rose and 1.8% failed for other reasons. On the whole, the research conducted in other European countries also showed that the two main causes of failure were flooding and direct or indirect disturbance by man. In addition, late nests have less chance of success.

Before concluding this brief examination, I would like to draw attention to a record, both interesting and pleasing, of some years standing; the recovery of a nesting kingfisher, ringed ten years previously. Although nothing precludes the existence of even older birds, this is the most elderly of those observed and ringed.

TERRITORY

*t*he kingfisher is a solitary bird for most of the year, throughout the entire period outside the breeding season. Later on I shall try to explain the reasons for this solitary existence, but for now I shall limit myself to the observation that during this long interval the kingfisher defends a feeding territory of variable size against intrusion by other kingfishers. It is as well to make clear that here I am referring to winter territory, which is generally smaller than the breeding territory defended by both partners during the summer. These strongly defended areas do not have precise dimensions because their extent depends on various elements such as the abundance of fish, the density of the resident population, the presence of banks suitable for nesting, etc.

The nesting territory is established in spring, probably by the male, which arrives a week or two before the female. Sometimes, however, the adult males remain in the breeding territory throughout the winter, as I have myself witnessed on several occasions. In the reserve of "Zelata", near Pavia, for three successive winters, I noted the presence of a male which also stayed there for the nesting period. His winter territory partly overlapped the summer one, which also comprised a separate feeding area, some 100 m distant from the nest. This feeding territory contained an organically cultivated ricefield in which the pair captured a great number of frogs to feed to their nestlings. The male was particularly aggressive in the central part of the territory, something shown by many researchers in various localities.

As far as behaviour at the boundaries is concerned, when I began my studies at Zelata, I unwittingly chose to settle near a small pool within the network containing bleak that was situated between the territories of two separate subjects. Because these were the first observations that I made in the zone, I did not know how many kingfishers were there, far less how the territories were allocated. In the space of a week, because of the tension provoked in the presence of the food resources at this point, not more than three bleak were caught. When I moved to about 300 m from the pool, within one of the two territories, the alarm calls ceased and the fish rapidly disappeared.

Left: The presence of a kingfisher is often betrayed by small pellets of undigested material that have been regurgitated. They are small pale oval balls that contain mainly scales and bones of fish

Pages 54-55. In its breeding territory the kingfisher can become aggressive towards other small birds. On p.54 a female drives away a wren. Page 55 shows two postures of threat-display

As I have said, the size of the territory is variable and from the different information obtained in Europe, it appears that in the nesting period, the space between the pairs can vary between about 300m and as far as 1km. Similar observations conducted in the former Soviet Union, more precisely in Estonia and Ryazan, have furnished rather different data, with a slightly larger distance between the pairs. In the first case, 15 pairs were found in about 18km of banks; in the second, the space between the nests was on average 1-2km. A particular case that occurred in Sweden involved pairs separated only by 125-200m, probably due to the absence of other suitable sites. In cases such as this, the extreme proximity provokes a state of tension which can prevent breeding success.

Taking account of the feeding areas as well, the dimensions of the territory increase, occupying on average a length of more than 800m, up to 1.5km. Part of this territory might include some areas of separate fishing, such as a small lake, a pool or spring, that, even if not visited every day but only occasionally, are strongly defended. It can also happen that the kingfisher is possessive about a perch and will confront other birds which alight there. This usually occurs when the branch is in the centre of a territory or near the nest. I remember a wren which had built its nest about 10m away from a pair of kingfishers, in the same bank. On the way to feeding its own nestlings, it landed once on the favourite branch of the kingfisher pair and began to sing. The female immediately chased it, adopting the typical "upright threat display" and succeeded in making the display obvious to the hide a few metres away.

VOICE AND CALLS

As I said a little earlier, the kingfisher often gives several loud and penetrating call notes while flying along its territory and, in particular, before returning to a perch. This serves to signal its presence to other kingfishers, which are thus warned to keep away. The call also serves to maintain contact with its mate during the nesting period, indicating its position within the territory, and with the young before and after fledging. The phrases vary according to the situation and behaviour, and can be distinguished as "contact calls", "alarm calls", "threat calls", "advertising calls", etc. To these ought to be added a true "song", which is richer in sounds and more varied, and of which I shall speak further in the chapter concerning nesting.

The calls are heard most frequently in spring and summer, while the birds become quieter in autumn and winter. Even though the phrases have been recorded, our interpretations do not take true account of various nuances which must have a precise significance. The calls are

described in many ways in different languages, but in summary, the kingfisher utters several different phrases of which I give only a few here. One of the most typical is the alarm call "kee kee" or "tjii tjii". The contact calls between partners can be rendered as "ti titi", or "tji tjii" and also "tjii tit tit tit tit".

In defence of the territory, before attacking, both the sexes sometimes emit a raucous "kritritrit" or "trrr trrr trrrtrrrtrrrtrrrtrrrtrrrtrrrtrrrtrrrt". Finally, the wide and varied repertoire of whistles and calls depends on the age of the kingfishers, from when they are nestlings until they become adults. It is not possible to describe them sufficiently well in writing. Therefore, I advise the reader who would like to examine these further to listen to some tape recordings.

The kingfisher is rather silent in autumn and winter, when it becomes solitary

ANTAGONISTIC

BEHAVIOUR

*l*ate that summer, the channel that ran through my property was no longer occupied by the usual female. What I feared most became reality when I discovered the taut net of a poacher slung between the banks of the channel, some hundred metres outside the boundary. There I found the remains of four kingfishers, one of which was the female who for the past three years had lived in my stretch of water. The stupidity of the hunter put paid to the friendship, the result of long and patient work, which had sprung up between me and the little bird. The female had acquired such confidence that she displayed towards me as if I were another kingfisher, like the aggressive posture she used sometimes to tell me to move away from "her" territory.

She was perfectly accustomed to all the photographic equipment, the noise of the shutter and the flashlights. She also connected the equipment with an abundance of fish for I was in the habit of putting some small live fish into the reserve before starting work. Her destruction was a particularly unfortunate event, above all from a purely sentimental aspect because I had a special affection for her.

Because altogether four individuals had died, this represented a not insignificant loss to the local population. In so far as it concerned my work, I had to wait until another bird took possession of the water course, in order to start work from the beginning again. I was fortunate; after a few weeks two juveniles of the year arrived, and immediately began to compete for the territory, allowing me to make a series of interesting and entertaining observations at the same time.

The first bird immediately discovered the reserve of fish which I always kept supplied near a bank of the channel. This I used only as a means of bait, while the photographs of the dives were taken in the channel itself, in free water. The branches of the trees and bushes overhanging the feeding reserve provided perches for the birds, allowing me to record other aspects of behaviour. I was able to note the presence of the second bird, which I shall call number 2, while observing the displays of the first, number 1. Initially, number 2 remained far from my hiding place and perched above the reserve, already occupied by the first.

The posture of number 1 changed as the days progressed; he devoted less time to feeding and assumed a characteristic position with the bill pointed slightly upwards. This is known as the "upright-threat display". The position of the body vaguely resembled that of a penguin, with plumage held close and sleek to the body, in a way to make the bird appear more streamlined and more elongated than normal. All this while it remained in profile or half-profile in respect of the position of number 2. There then followed another posture, which consisted of hunching the shoulders, pushing the bill forward or slightly upwards, but never directly towards the rival. The bill was slightly open, moved repeatedly and slowly, in a way that described a sideways arc, while the bird stared directly and intently towards its antagonist.

When number 2 decided to abandon the highest branches of the willow and landed near the perch of number 1, the two birds assumed a more menacing posture, the "forward-threat display". In this phase number 1 emitted raucous and intense threat calls, while both turned sideways, with the neck and bill along the perch. They stayed in this position, a little more than a metre from each other, sometimes slowly rolling the body horizontally, each in the direction of the rival.

These were warnings given by the two contenders before they eventually attacked. This ritual, consisting of slow and precise movements, reminded me of another spectacle, equally slow, precise and rich in symbolism, the Japanese Noh theatre, where Shite invites Waki to dance. Although the precise meaning of individual displays of the kingfisher are obscure, it is evident that the profile position and the movement of the head and neck make the "offensive weapon", the bill, obvious to the antagonist.

All species of animals which have developed "weapons" in the course of evolution, that is are physically adapted not only to kill their prey, but

Pages 60-63 show ritual threat displays in a confrontation between kingfishers.
Pages 60-61: aggressive posturing generally starts with the "upright-threat" display followed by the "forward-threat" display

Right: the attack on a stuffed dummy rival is brought about with great speed and precision

also one of their own species, have at the same time developed mechanisms for inhibitory behaviour, necessary for survival. In the case of a social animal like the wolf, for example, the posture of submission on the part of the weaker releases inhibitory behaviour in the stronger. In normal conditions, the stronger of the two does not sink its weapons, its teeth, in the neck that its weaker adversary deliberately exposes.

The kingfisher, like other animals that live in isolation for a large part of the year, has developed a different, but equally valid, mechanism: flight. The weaker of the two flies away, followed by its rival as far as the boundary of its territory.

After the ritual warnings, the attack followed, number 2 took flight and number 1 returned to his own perch, in front of my own hiding place. However, whereas the old female killed by the poacher had rapidly imposed her dominance, here the skirmishes continued for three days. Such a protracted contest is not very common, and was probably the result of the inexperience of the two contenders and of the abundance of fish in the reserve. The following day number 2 was more intrepid, the rituals became briefer, and the attacks, although they were conducted according to a precise pattern, became more frequent. However, the ceremony that precedes the aggressive phase is not limited to the postures of the two juveniles, but can be more varied, like the combatants, which can even display in water.

When the two rivals found themselves on the same branch, or at a distance of about a metre from each other, there were frequent and simultaneous changes of position, alternating between the upright- and forward-threat displays. As well as the various postures of aggressive behaviour which I have observed, I have noted an attitude very similar to the stretching that the kingfisher makes in the moment before jumping up to its perch. It involves curving the back forwards, a way of showing to the rival and making more obvious the brilliant blue-turquoise colour of the back and rump, together with opening the wings and flicking them backwards, or fanning them slowly. This display was sometimes accompanied by opening and swinging the tail sideways or moving it backwards and forwards. As I have said, the threat display frequently precedes attack and chase in flight, accompanied by the aggressive call.

Contenders intent on holding on to their position have been known to seize each other by the bill, and finish up in the water, where they continue to fight. During one dispute over winter territory, a fleeing kingfisher was observed diving into water (see also Miramonti's account on page 79), followed by the rival in a series of dives and emergences. In similar circumstances each one may try to drown its adversary by holding the head under water, but cases of this are infrequent and I believe that the death of a combatant or its wounding is a very rare event and according to my records, has never actually been seen. Disputes are

The kingfisher tries to dislodge an intruder (a stuffed bird) from the perch

After several attempts it grabs the neck of the presumed rival in its beak

Attacks are generally aimed at the neck

generally brief, but can be repeated spasmodically over several days.

I realised how the attacks were directed from the photographs I took during the nesting period recording the aggression of a pair of kingfishers towards a stuffed specimen. The scuffles were so rapid that they were difficult to distinguish precisely with the naked eye.

It was the female that initiated the attacks, probably because the male was occupied with feeding the nestlings. From various images taken at the speed of f5 per second, I noticed that the attack was generally directed at the neck, sometimes at the head or at the wings. At the end, the female forcefully grasped the neck of the puppet for more than a minute, trying at the same time to push it over, to dislodge it from the perch to which it was attached. By contrast, under natural conditions numbers 1 and 2 abated the attacks, from time to time opposing bills. The bills locked on to each other and the attacker tried to dislodge its rival from the branch on which it was perched. At this point I record an amusing episode. The second day I arrived by bicycle at the fields near the area under dispute where I dismounted quickly and silently. Number 1 was grappling on its branch in an erect position but with its head bent down, the bill locked with that of number 2, which was hanging down with open wings, trying to pull its rival from its perch. They remained like that for some moments, then became aware of my presence and flew away.

The dispute was by now in the last act and it was in fact number 1 that left the field, followed by number 2 as far as the boundary of its fishing territory. At this point the roles were perfectly defined and number 1 stayed on the outside limits, entering furtively only when the other, satiated, went away.

One could question the significance of aggression in the life of this species and ask if it would not be more convenient for rivals to live within the same territory as do other more social species. The following account may help to explain why this is not so. The winter of 1984 was marked by a period of exceptional cold. For some days the temperature was less than -15°C in many areas of Lombardy. Large areas of the water courses iced over and exceptional numbers of kingfishers died. I remember that the survivors tenaciously defended their positions in the small pockets where water moved sufficiently to prevent it from icing over, but not so much as to impede fishing. Because of the extreme conditions and the scarcity of food, the kingfishers' balance of energy was extremely precarious, to the point where if it had been necessary to share the few areas left with others, probably all would have died. I remember one of these birds, after two unsuccessful dives into icy water, failing to re-emerge at the third attempt. It would certainly have been drowned if it had not been netted out. I opened its bill with two fingers and slipped in a bleak, which it promptly swallowed, then I warmed it up and set it free.

The female of the kingfisher pair attacks the stuffed bird after a series of threat postures. Territorial scuffles can also take place in water where the contenders dive and re-emerge repeatedly, often with their bills locked together. The contests rarely result in injury; the weaker of the two simply retreats from its rival's territory

That winter of 1984 was an extreme case, but even in normal climatic conditions, the energy balance of a predator like the kingfisher does not allow much margin for error. The fish are in fact less stupid than one would expect and after several dives from the bird, time passes before they show themselves again. For its part, the kingfisher is a "stabbing" hunter - it does not pursue its prey, but suddenly strikes while the fish is still or moving only slowly. This method of hunting, aiming directly at the prey, means that there is no profit in collaboration, because the hunters disturb each other and the chance of success diminishes.

This is why the kingfisher subdivides its fishing territory with intraspecific aggression, to ensure better distribution and therefore optimal survival of the population. The food resources are divided between individuals and dispersal ensures the occupation of territories not yet populated.

This partly explains the success that this species has had in colonising vast areas of the world. Moreover, a similar mechanism favours the reproduction of the strongest and healthiest individuals, with a consequent improvement in the quality of the population. Naturally, as well as these advantages there are some disadvantages, as the expense of energy determines the physical conflicts, which nevertheless have limited duration and almost always finish without wounding or damage. The advantages derived from aggressive behaviour amply outweigh the disadvantages and once the territory is established, there is more time for normal activities without further disturbance to the balance of energy.

In conclusion, it is also worth noting that the two partners also hunt separately during the nesting period.

After having finally toppled its
rival, the kingfisher perches
above it in a display of dominance

COLOURS

& MIMICRY

*t*here are days in February when the air is clear and the light is particularly intense and sharp. They are cold, clear days which we would call fine: a simple way of describing the absence of mist in the atmosphere and of the impurities that increasingly afflict it. It was a day like this, and the rime covering the grass crunched underfoot. The contrasts along the pathway were particularly strong and everything was a more intense colour than normal. Some 20 metres to the right of my hide I saw the little wooden bridge that I used to cross the channel - it was covered in frost. In the middle of the bridge, on the edge, perched the female of the preceding year which had established herself in my stretch of water. The heat from her legs and body had melted the crystals of frost around her.

It was one of those rare days in which everything went smoothly: the gunfire of hunters could not be heard, the locals were working elsewhere, I was not expecting visitors and in spite of the piercing cold, the sun warmed my camouflaged hide as if it were a small greenhouse. I fixed the binoculars on the tripod and started to watch.

Below the immobile kingfisher, a tiny wren was rummaging frenetically in search of insect eggs and small larvae in the mass of dry vegetation brought down by the wind and rain of the past few days. Its brown plumage blended in well with its surroundings and it was unceasing in its search for food. The whole scene I was observing presented the marked and, at the same time, richly significant contrasts that only nature can offer.

The kingfisher stayed still, except for some almost imperceptible movements of the head and shoulders. She was waiting for the exact moment to launch her decisive strike at prey much bigger than that of the wren, not only in an absolute sense, but also in respect of the proportions of both birds. Two species that live in the same habitat, like the kingfisher and the wren, are not necessarily similar.

Many forces have moulded the anatomy, physiology and behaviour of each creature, especially among the predators. The birds, in particular, first had to make their most important conquest, flight. As well as having developed a streamlined and, above all, aerodynamic structure, they have

The beautiful shade of the back comes from the microstructure of the feathers, called Tyndall blue. The colour is the result of a physical phenomenon (see pp. 76-77) and is not due to pigmentation, unlike the reddish parts of the plumage

The colour of the plumage can change according to the angle of incidence of light, as can also be seen in the photos on pages 78-79

succeeded in modifying themselves during the course of evolution in other vital ways. First is the "conquest" of food and therefore, for the kingfisher and the wren, predation. But prey creatures are not all the same: their structure, distribution, the possibility of flight or defence, the "swift riposte", all have to be guarded against when a predator is hunting; all are fundamental in the ecological balance between prey and predators. One can therefore say that the prey has moulded the predators and the prey in turn has been modified in order to evade capture.

It is a continuous game of surprise, a kind of armaments race among the species. Over millions of years of evolution, the kingfisher has chosen for prey relatively intelligent and speedy vertebrates (fish), present usually only in small numbers in each environment. Often it follows shoals and is therefore difficult to locate, being situated in small areas of fishing territory easily controlled by one individual. As we have seen, this explains the presence of a territory with clear feeding (rather than breeding) functions.

In addition, the hunting technique of the kingfisher and the majority of the Alcedinidae is highly effective. It is much better, once having spotted a shoal of fish, to stop and prepare an ambush. Perched on a branch, immobile, the kingfisher is much less visible to fish. Here is another selective force which has imposed its own influence and moulded behaviour. As has been shown for many other species, this bird adopts

what is definitely the best strategy for feeding. It is, however, a strategy that depends on many other variable factors, some of which have been discussed previously.

Now let us see how the wren differs from the kingfisher and why its behaviour is much more obvious. Even though it is a smaller and much better camouflaged bird than the kingfisher, it is also much easier to see. The rapid movements betray its presence even to a distant observer. This is because in comparison with the kingfisher, its prey (small insects, arachnids and other invertebrates) are widely and almost uniformly distributed throughout the environment and it does not need to defend a territory exclusively for feeding. Attempting to chase off other wrens when there is a small spider every few square centimetres would be illogical and wasteful. This does not mean to say that the wren does not have a territory but it is more closely connected with the breeding season.

The incessant, busy movements of the wren are also due to the fact that its prey cannot really run away. It is therefore possible to search in a continuous way, without resting. As a prey item, a little insect, for example, does not give a wren a return in terms of energy similar to that of a fish; this is another reason for searching to be continuous. It is a case of whether to have a continuous supply of energy such as one sweet a minute, or a rich and nutritious cake every two or three days.

Other considerations are more obvious. The shape of a predatory animal is also an essential factor in the capture of prey: a kingfisher is a perfect diving machine, while a wren has a form that is ideal for insinuating itself into the smallest crevices in search of food. The two bills are so different that one could be forgiven for doubting whether they are the same structure. In addition, the kingfisher's wings and those of the wren lend themselves to a different way of flying. In sum, the environment and in particular the prey mould both the form and behaviour of each predatory bird much more than it would be possible to imagine just by observing a kingfisher sitting still on a branch and a wren searching incessantly through the vegetation below.

Is there not a contradiction in the kingfisher's brilliant colours and its need not to be noticed? This is one of the infinite number of cases in which nature has had to mediate and it has taken the best course between two contrasting needs. Each species is modified for a compromise that meets the various essentials of reproduction, defence, nutrition, migration, etc.

The kingfisher, in comparison with mammals, has exceptionally good sight, so that in resolving detail, perception of colours and the messages by which it communicates, it relies on sight more than sound. In birds, various signals connected with behaviour such as territoriality, courtship, etc, are linked to the disposition, quality and brilliance of colour markings. In particular, in the tropical zones, the sheer numbers of species has made the conspicuous diversification of colours necessary, in order immediately to recognise one individual from another. The kingfisher, as we have seen, is connected to the Palearctic by the islands of Malaysia and has had to modify slightly its sparkling livery to adapt to new needs. But the variations are minimal, because its plumage is also suitable for our own environment. First of all, it nests in holes that are almost always inaccessible to predators and it does not need an inconspicuous plumage like those species, which, for example, nest on the ground. In the second place, we shall see that a predator could have just as much difficulty in noticing it as its prey does.

However, first let us examine more deeply the chromatic secrets of its plumage. The colouration of the kingfisher's upperparts has purely physical origins and is brought about by the absorption and refraction of light. It is a curious fact that a true blue pigment does not exist in birds, although this colour is diffused more in the kingfisher and other species, like the bee-eater, roller and some passeriformes, etc.

Observing the barbs of the blue feathers under the microscope, it can be seen that they possess a particular structure, called Tyndall blue by British ornithologists and Blaustruktur by those in Germany. They are covered with a refractive sheath of keratin under which there is a succession of cells, perforated by a number of tiny holes, situated according to a particular linear composition in one or more rows. This construction eliminates the components at the high frequency of the luminous spectrum - red; and reflects those at the low frequency - blue.

Moreover, the red rays come to be absorbed by an underlayer of melanin. The varying tones of blue or blue-green are therefore determined by the dimensions, thickness, disposition and numbers of the holes. This explains the diverse shades of blue in the various species and in the different parts of the plumage and their more or less accentuated brightness and chromatic purity. For this reason, the plumage of the upperparts of the kingfisher presents a complete series of chromatic variations on the theme of blue-green, with a marvellous stripe of turquoise-blue down the middle of the back and rump.

This splendid livery and its ability to change colour from turquoise-blue to emerald green is due to the angle of the light. In the underparts, instead, the colour is pigmented and is less splendid.

Despite its brilliant colouration, the kingfisher is well camouflaged in its natural habitat

Now that we have discovered the chromatic secrets of the kingfisher we can resume the discussion on mimicry.

It can be easily be imagined how, from the point of view of a fish, the usual prey of the kingfisher, the brick-red underparts might be confused with a dry leaf. Instead, from on high, as observed by a predator in flight, the azure-blue of the upperparts camouflages it well not only against water, above which it is generally perched, but, strangely, also with the vegetation. If one also considers its immobility, one can understands how for both prey and predator the kingfisher is not easy to discern. Certainly, I have frequently failed to see one even when it was close. In practice, animals that on their own would be conspicuous are the opposite when they are put into the context of their environment; think of a tree-frog. Moreover, in the shade of vegetation, where the kingfisher perches most of the time, its brilliance and colour are less vivid. In sum, the kingfisher's camouflage, that seems in contradiction with the gaudiness of its plumage, makes predation a comparatively rare event. Without doubt, the attention

that the kingfisher gives to everything that moves, together with its stillness when perched, are contributory factors.

My friend Angelo Miramonti, who has collaborated in this book with the photographs taken inside the nest tunnel, told me about an attempted predation on the part of a hooded crow observed from the inside of my own hide. The crow attacked the kingfisher and chased it in flight, close to the water surface. The two birds passed quickly in front of the hide, veering towards the bank opposite the water course. Here the kingfisher flew into a dense bush, disappearing from Miramonti's view, who told me he heard the noise of wings fluttering against the leaves.

Immediately afterwards, the kingfisher passed anew before the hide, diving suddenly into the water while the crow was above it. It emerged in the opposite direction, and successfully escaped.

I believe that is one of the very rare observations of attack of a predator on a kingfisher, although other episodes of predation with more dramatic results could happen inside the nesting tunnel, as we shall see later.

F O O D

& F E E D I N G   H A B I T S

*I*made my most interesting observations on the kingfisher's fishing behaviour some years ago at my property at Veneto. The place was ideal, as I have already said in the chapter on Movements, but in recent years human activity has been devastating. The region has become rapidly less and less natural, intensive agriculture has occupied every square centimetre of territory, pits are filled in to make areas available for cultivation, the hedges, sometimes hundreds of years old, that border the area, have been grubbed up, and the water courses have been straightened and canalised. The water table is noticeably lower and the water drawn up by wells is polluted by factories and agricultural run-off. The indigenous hedges and the trees that form the boundaries of my study area remain, but the general ecological degradation is evident even here, and the channel dries out for increasingly longer periods, while because of eutrophication, the water surface is covered with vegetation. The kingfisher population is gradually moving away to other territories, because a growing number of water courses, in which this habitat was particularly rich, remain dry.

This state of affairs has destroyed much of the special atmosphere that characterised my last weeks at Veneto, even though the swallows and hoopoes, together with many other species, return each year to nest. For this reason I had to transfer my studies to some areas of Ticino Park, near Milan (where I completed my work), but I have not given up the search for a solution to reintroduce water to my channel or at least to a part of it. Since in the periods of greatest drought the water table is about half a metre under the pebble-covered riverbed, and it is relatively easy to reach, the idea came to me to excavate a small pit and put in about thirty bleak. I was certain that the kingfisher, having had to move about a kilometre away due to the lack of fish, would see the small area of water

The pictures on pages 81-99
show the hunting action
of the kingfisher

while flying across the countryside to reach the different fishing zones. The second day I noticed that the numbers of bleak had been noticeably reduced, and on a twig a little above the pool glittered some minuscule fish-scales.

There was no doubt that the small food source had been found, because the scales were an unmistakable sign of the presence of a kingfisher. The bird violently batters fish against the branch on which it is perched, holding them firmly in the bill, before swallowing them. In this way, they are rapidly killed and a certain number of scales are left sticking to the wood, so that favourite perches literally glisten. I recall that it was the end of August when I dug the first pit, but then the water table also lowered in other periods of the year, finally drying out even my channel, which was the deepest of the surrounding watercourses. Each time, a kingfisher located the pit and caught the bleak. This bird, that obviously does not have the structure of a soaring bird, completed flights at a height greater than one might have expected it to be capable of, as it usually flies close to the water surface. In reality, its ability to find even the smallest area of water is proverbial.

In support of this, I remember an amusing fact that I read in a book, written by Professor Scortecci, who was director of the Museum of Natural History in Milan. He recounted that one of his collaborators, the well known ornithologist Professor Moltoni, was informed by a telephone call that for some days a little bird had been catching fish in some of the open-air tanks at the Civic Aquarium. This naturally surprised Moltoni because the Aquarium was a building that stood in the centre of Milan. In the surrounding gardens were several tanks containing fish. The little bird, a kingfisher, was caught with a net, ringed and released by Professor Moltoni some kilometres away along a water course. After a few hours, the ringed kingfisher was fishing again in the tanks of the Aquarium. It was caught once more, taken some thirty kilometres away and did not return to the city. Without doubt, it must have flown quite high to discover a small area of water in the centre of Milan.

Nevertheless, we cannot put forward any precise theories on the flying performances of the kingfisher, because there is a lack of observations to refer to, and our knowledge of the dynamics of birdflight is fairly scarce.

Certainly the kingfisher does not have the structure of a frigate, a bird with a wingspan of 1.20m, whose skeleton weighs only 110g; less than its plumage. However, other birds, like geese and ducks, in spite of a less favourable weight to wing surface ratio, can complete long journeys at high altitude. This account gives us an idea of the kingfisher's ability to find new fishing areas and as we shall see, it is equally skillful underwater, where it obtains its prey.

Even if freshwater fish constitute most of its food, the kingfisher uses other aquatic habitats that can provide food in the form of insects,

*Above and overleaf: when its
prey is far enough below the water
surface, the kingfisher dives
vertically. When coming out
of the water, the bird beats its
wings against the surface and
immediately thrusts the prey
upwards*

amphibians, crustaceans, molluscs and saltwater fish. Sometimes, but more rarely, it takes terrestrial insects. It is not a specialised predator, but catches many different species. Nevertheless, the main food resource is fish, both in number and, above all, in weight, that is, biomass. It is from fish that the kingfisher obtains most of its energy requirements, and fish comprise about 60% to 90% of the various prey animals, according to the type of territory.

Many studies have been made of the kingfisher's diet, most of them based on analysis of pellets, which are small, whitish, oval balls of indigestible material regurgitated after digestion. Of course, such analyses do not provide data on the prey which is digested completely, and of this I shall speak further subsequently.

In practice, because the prey with indigestible parts is usually fish, the examination of some small bones found in the pellets, such as the preoperculum or the lower jaw, makes it possible to determine both the species and its dimensions. For example, one of these studies, conducted during the nesting seasons of 1975 to 1977 in the river Lesse in Belgium has furnished information on the feeding of both adults and young. Nestlings less than 10 days old were fed on little fish less than 4cm long, while the greater part of the prey was between 4 and 7cm in length and the largest encountered was 10cm long. This indicated, as was expected, that the small species with slow growth suffered from predation by kingfishers throughout their lives, while larger species with rapid growth soon succeeded in avoiding predation. Moreover, the same studies have shown the presence of tiny molluscs, on average less than 2mm, which are found in the stomachs of fish. In addition, observations made in England in the pellets collected from the tunnel and chamber after nesting have provided similar results. (It is interesting to report here, that in order not to damage the tunnel which the birds would probably re-use the following year, the material was collected by washing it out for an hour with a 10% solution of oxygenated water.)

The identification of prey is correlated with place, because it is clear that the species can vary noticeably from one stream to another, or from one region to another. In England, for example, a majority of minnows (*Phoxinus phoxinus*) is found in amounts varying from 46% to 80%, followed by sticklebacks (*Gasterosteus aculeatus*) with percentages varying from 17% to 45%. The results obtained on the river Lesse in Belgium on a total of 14,475 items of fish, produced instead 90% bullheads (*Cottus gobio*) and carp (*Cyprinidae*). These results are very different, but in both cases the pike (*Esox lucius*), for example, is almost absent, whereas from a study in Italy, on a length of the river Ticino, pike comprised about 22% of the diet. Thus the kingfisher will take any species of fish, varying in size from little more than a centimetre up to 10cm, which ventures near the water surface during daylight.

As I said, fish are not the only source of food, and, for example, during the nesting period in May, a not insignificant part of the prey brought to the nest consisted of small and average-sized frogs. That fact is quickly explained as not far away were ricefields, typical of the Lombardy plain, that were full of frogs. At other times I observed and photographed the capture of dragonfly larvae *(Aeshna cyanea)*, tadpoles and even a newt. In practice, every aquatic organism of appropriate dimensions can fall prey.

Nevertheless, because not every creature swallowed has indigestible parts, a study was made in Spain directly upon the digestive tract of the birds. For this research 96 kingfishers that had been killed by hunting were used (the usefulness of this study certainly does not justify the stupidity of hunters who have eliminated so many birds). The data recovered provided information not only on the fish, but also on the amphibians, crustaceans and insects, some of which were totally digested. The greatest percentage was constituted of water bugs *(Hemiptera)* and in particular backswimmers *(Notonectidae)*; in second place were Odonata, including an adult dragonfly.

Bear in mind that the composition of the diet varies according to place, and that the kingfisher is a good sampler. In order to have an idea of the quantity of species consumed, here is a short and incomplete list beginning with freshwater fish: bleak *(Alburnus alburnus alborella)*, minnow *(Phoxinus phoxinus)*, bullhead *(Cottus gobio)*, stickleback *(Gasterosteus aculeatus)*, loach *(Cobitis taenia)*, roach *(Rutilus rubilio)*, dace *(Leuciscus cephalus)*, trout *(Salmo trutta)*, pike *(Esox lucius)*, perch *(Perca fluviatilis)*, barb *(Barbus barbus)*, grayling *(Thymallus thymallus)*, mosquito fish *(Gambusia affinis)*, crucian carp *(Carassius carassius)*, nase *(Chondrostoma toxostoma)*, gudgeon *(Gobio gobio)*, rudd *(Scardinius erythrophthalmus)*, soufie *(Leuciscus souffia)*, freshwater blenny *(Blennius fluviatilis)*, and ruffe *(Acerina cernua)*.

For saltwater fish, data are scarce, so I shall confine myself to four species, while bearing in mind that the salty diet can also be very varied: sand smelt *(Atherina hepsetus)*, shore clingfish *(Lepadogaster lepadogaster)*, burnbot *(Lota lota)*, and bass *(Dicenthrarcus labrax)*.

Amphibians. As mentioned above, I have seen frogs and tadpoles *(Rana esculenta)* caught several times and a newt *(Triturus vulgaris)* once.

An unusual occurrence. The kingfisher has failed in its aim and emerges from its dive with a pebble

Pages 94-95 show a dive into shallow water. In order to arrest its diving action immediately below the surface, the kingfisher holds its wings open

Left and above: in a deeper dive, the wings are closed and the kingfisher assumes a much more streamlined, penetrating shape that is maintained until it strikes its prey

*The bird arrives at the bottom with
its wings closed, and opens them
only at the last moment*

Arthropods comprised a modest part of the diet, especially in terms of biomass. Generally, the predated species are those whose larval stages are aquatic, for example dragonfly nymphs, but also caddis flies *(Trichoptera)*, mayflies *(Ephemeroptera)*, and Hemiptera like the backswimmer *(Notonecta glauca)* and the water scorpion *(Nepa cinerea)*. In addition, I have seen spiders and crustaceans caught.

I shall not report anything else about the various species caught in freshwater or the sea but shall now go on to discuss feeding methods.

Each kingfisher has its own characteristics and feeding methods and once it has established its territory along a stream, it learns intimately every suitable place for fishing, every detail of the branch on which it is perched and concentrates its attention on whatever moves in the area. Because of its particular diet, the kingfisher has much more time to dedicate to the exploration of its territory than could a small insectivore in constant search of insects throughout the day. Fifteen bleak, 5-7cm long, per day, are sufficient for the kingfisher, which can devote its time to the intensive exploration of its territory. This is an activity fundamental to survival given the great variability of the streams and the constant displacement of shoals of fish. Generally, little fish congregate in shallow water in summer, while in winter they prefer to stay a little deeper in calm water or with only a weak current. According to the seasons, the fish move up or downstream towards the areas in which, during the periods of drought, there remain pockets of water of greater or lesser size, which become important food reserves.

The kingfisher has exceptional sight to locate rapidly not only each new possible feeding area, but also a single fish in spite of rippling water, the reflections on the surface and the camouflage of the fish, which are usually darker or lighter in colour according to their environment. As I have just said, prey is not only from fresh water, given that a certain number of birds establish themselves along river estuaries, coast and islands. In support of this I made a study from September 1990 during a brief holiday in the nature reserve known as "Lo Zingaro" in Sicily. While I seemed to hear the characteristic call of the kingfisher, I believed I was confusing the calls of some local woodland birds, because I did not hear the sound more distinctly. A little later a kingfisher burst out in flight from a crag some 100 metres away, and flew towards the coast, passing close to the water a few metres from me. I noted that its perch was in a fig of India and regretted that I had not brought my camera.

Right and overleaf:
to re-emerge the kingfisher uses its
wings and presses its bill down
against its breast

Looking through a diving mask, I saw also a dense shoal of little silver fish Latterini *(Atherina hepsetus)* that swam just beneath the water surface and assumed these were probably the prey, even though I did not actually see one caught.

No matter whether the prey belongs to salt or freshwater, the quantity of fish consumed is truly remarkable and many times have I observed the kingfisher swallow four bleak of about 6cm one after another before being satiated. This happened especially in winter when the bird dived in the tank in which I had placed several bleak of average size. For a creature 17cm long and about 40g weight, this was the equivalent of a man weighing 70kg eating 17kg of meat in one sitting.

Digestion usually takes place on the same perch where the fish was eaten. It concludes with the expulsion from the bill of the pellet containing the indigestible parts. During this phase the kingfisher remains on the branch, absently following the movements of the fish, and after not more than half an hour, it is ready to renew activity.

When fish move out from the shore into open water, or when there are no perches, the kingfisher can hover. It remains suspended in the air, using its wings to generate enough power to give it sufficient lift without forward movement. In the reserve of Zelata, in Ticino Park, where I was able to make my most recent observations and take photographs, there is a particular point where the kingfisher tends to hover. It is at the confluence of two streams, forming a vortex and a pool, almost in the middle of the water course. In this small area, the nutrients suspended in the water currents attract fish. The water is about 60 cm deep and the kingfisher has to obtain a good speed to reach the prey, which usually stay at the bottom. I remember that sometimes it hovered for more than 15 seconds, at a height of about two metres, as if it were suspended by an invisible string until the exact moment of diving. This type of flight, of which the true master is the hummingbird, demands a great deal of energy and pronounced wing movement. Not all birds can manage it, although many are successful while flying , in which case the strain is minimised.

Let us now look in a little more depth at the techniques of fishing, particularly the sequence of actions.

In the course of evolution, each living being has developed in its own genetic code all the information necessary for survival and has formed in consequence its own particular physiology and behaviour. For a predator like the kingfisher, specialised in hunting fairly intelligent animals with rapid reflexes such as fish, it is essential that the action of catching should be as effective and efficient as possible. This means that the trajectory at the moment of impact should be as precise as possible, coupled with the minimum expenditure of energy. One of the most interesting aspects of this adaptation is the ability to take account of the error of refraction

When there are no suitable perches
available, the kingfisher hovers
before diving

between air and water. Under a simple law of optical physics, a fish, like every other creature beneath the water surface, is not really in the position that it appears to be to those outside, but is displaced to a certain extent. This happens when the water surface is observed obliquely, but directly from above the effect is nullified. (Whoever has tried to snatch at something under the water will be aware of the phenomenon.) The kingfisher possesses the ability to modify its trajectory when it is not perpendicular to the surface, in proportion to the angle and depth at which it locates its prey.

In other words, it is as if it has an ability to make calculations, allowing for and correcting the incidence of refraction. In reality, because of the size of the prey and bill, even a small error is enough to foil its aim. When the fish is situated at a depth of more than 40 cm, the attacking dive is always vertical, to reduce the flight course and therefore the time involved to the shortest possible. Do not forget that fish have very rapid reflexes, and muscles adapted to move suddenly the moment the kingfisher hits the water surface. As can be seen from the pictures on pages 96-97, the bird assumes a particularly aerodynamic form, holding the wings behind it to form a delta shape, and some milliseconds later, when the bill has already completely penetrated the water, the points of the remiges advance, making the bird even more streamlined, with two verticals in the bill and the points of the wings. This particular aspect, which I have photographed several times with special apparatus, is typical of the strike in deep water. When, by contrast, the fish is in shallow water – between 20 and 30 cm – the wings are not held like a wedge, but are held in delta-shape, as you can clearly see in the photographs on pages 94-95. In this case, in fact, it has to be able to brake first, in order to avoid collision with the bottom. When prey is found in a few centimetres of water, the kingfisher brakes with the breast and with outspread wings and tail, as can be seen in the photographs on pages 101 & 103. It can also happen that it snatches a fish from the surface, without diving, but passing in flight with a "touch and go".

It is also interesting to look at what happens from the moment the kingfisher jumps from its perch, to when it returns with a fish in its bill. Hardly has it settled on the branch than it has completed some characteristic movements of the head and shoulders from side to side. My interpretation is that perhaps this allows it to observe from different angles, making it easier to locate prey which may be obscured by reflections. Immediately afterwards it concentrates on a precise spot. Discovering possible prey, the kingfisher clearly demonstrates a noticeable tension, the feathers sleeked against the body and every muscle taut.

The actions of the prey are constantly followed, as can be seen from the movement of the head and bill, while the tail is moved to and fro and the pale marks at the sides of the neck enlarge and diminish. At the same

time, the kingfisher makes small jumps, adjustments, on its branch and short, rapid sideways movements. Immediately before it attacks, its wings move out imperceptibly from the body, or more rarely, open out, beating. Suddenly, the bird dives towards the water, obtaining the necessary speed with a few wingbeats. If the perch is too low and the water deep, the kingfisher first flies upwards, then it dives, exactly as if it had been hovering. The deepest dive observed was over a metre, while the dive from the highest position was of 11m. During the flight before impact with the water surface, the eyes are open and the bill closed or slightly open. Underwater, the nictitating membrane slides over the eyes and the bill opens like a pair of scissors, perpendicular to the axis of the fish that is reached as impetus subsides, without moving the wings. The bird brakes at the last moment, spreading wings and tail, while seizing the prey. Having made a capture, the kingfisher jumps vertically to the surface, with the back uppermost and the bill pressed to the breast. The jump is assisted by natural buoyancy, air trapped in the plumage and some wingbeats, as if the bird were flying under water. The head and part of the body emerge before the bill is taken from the breast, then it thrusts the prey strongly upwards, holding it firmly, as can be seen in the photographs on pages 87-89. It finally regains the perch, helped by the push of the wings on the water surface, an action that involves a major

Above and overleaf: a kingfisher swallows a fish on its usual perch, recognisable by the glistening fish scales

expense of energy. At this point, if the fish is small, it is swallowed immediately. Otherwise, if it is big, it is violently battered against the branch with rapid rotating movements of the head, until it is finally killed. Observations of this action show that it is always the head of the fish that is struck against the branch and not the tail. There can be as many as 47 "bashes" before the bird decides to swallow the prey, but even so the fish is sometimes still alive when it is swallowed and its last throes in the stomach visibly disturb the kingfisher on its perch.

Fish are always swallowed headfirst, so that the scales, gills and fins and in the case of the stickleback, the spines, are in the best position and do not impede ingestion. Many observations have related practically 100% success in fishing attempts in clear and calm water, but when the prey is sufficiently deep, things change. Especially in winter, when the cold reduces energy, there are more unsuccessful attempts and the young of the year are particularly prone to fail, thus paying the price of high mortality. In support of catching attempts that fail, I recall having seen and photographed a kingfisher emerging twice with a stone. Evidently the fish succeeded in fleeing at the last moment, while the bill closed on a small pebble (see page 93). On other occasions, by contrast, it emerged with two little fish, one of which, inevitably, fell into the water while the other was being swallowed.

The fish is rapidly killed with several blows against the perch and then swallowed headfirst so that the scales and fins do not present any resistance

Even after many dives, the plumage is always perfectly dry. Such impermeability is obtained by using the bill to spread over the feathers a particularly water-repellent oil from the preen-gland. Each feather is selected by the bill and where it cannot reach, like on the head, the kingfisher uses its feet. This operation also serves to adjust any feathers that are out of place and make them fit for flying again. Each feather is in fact constructed of hundreds of filaments called barbs, each one of which carries in turn hundreds of other minuscule filaments, called barbules, furnished with microscopic hooks. The barbules are hooked to each other and when for whatever reason the structure is disrupted, with a swift stroke of the bill, the tiny filaments are joined up, just like a zip. Preening, as it is called, is one of the most important activities for survival, and as the plumage consists of thousands of individual feathers and plumes, one can understand why the kingfisher devotes some two hours a day to this operation.

Another function of preening is probably relaxation, a way of returning to normal behaviour after a stressful, or abnormal situation. The kingfisher will preen after episodes such as disputes over territory, repeated failure of fishing attempts, tension caused by the sighting of a predator, etc.

B R E E D I N G

*t*he first incident of breeding that I observed, some 15 years ago, happened in a bank of the channel that runs through my property. I recall that the kingfishers began to excavate on 15th March, in the clayey wall that I had already prepared. A bank had slipped after a violent rainfall, revealing a tract of the tunnel excavated by a water vole *(Arvicola terrestris)*. I had made a vertical and smooth surface about two metres square around the hole, so that it should be inaccessible to mammals. The kingfisher pair used the short, perpendicular excavation, not more than 30 cm deep. I decided to make it another 15cm longer, slightly sloping upwards up to the nesting chamber. Before giving a more detailed description of the excavation of the nest, it is, however, more logical to explain the other aspects of this interesting phase in the life of the kingfisher, from courtship to the time when the young leave the nest.

In central southern Europe, the period of nesting can last longer than six months, while in the north the average duration is at least a month. Such long periods can occur when there are three successive broods, an event which happens infrequently; usually they are one or two broods.

In central Europe work on the tunnel begins during the first two weeks of March and the young of the last brood leave the nest at the latest around 10th October. If there are two broods, as happens in most cases, the last nestlings fledge towards the end of July. In northern and eastern Europe, the season begins later, around the first two weeks of April, while in England, it starts at the beginning of March and then finishes towards the end of July.

During the initial period of pair formation, the territorial instinct has gradually to yield to the stimulus to breed. What appears so simple and natural to us, is probably made difficult because of the instinct to fly away. Do not forget that the kingfisher is a solitary bird for most of the

During courtship there are
traces of aggression

year, because this is the most successful solution to its survival. For this reason, the aggressive instinct remains latent at least in the initial phase of courtship, so much so that on several occasions I have observed a tension between the partners, as the male advances within bill range of the female.

The first approaches between birds prospecting for mates usually happen towards the end of February, before construction of the tunnel has started. During pair formation, the territory around the nest resounds with penetrating calls, accompanied by the flight chases between male and female.

Sometimes the male, perched on a higher branch than normal, utters his advertising calls every two or three minutes. These calls can be described in several ways, but I think the most realistic transcription is "chi-kee chi-kee". When the female arrives, the calls become even more frequent as she advances, and it is usually just at this point that the series of flight chases are initiated, accompanied by vociferous contact-alarm calls: "ti', tit" "ti', tit".

The flight chases develop in various ways and can involve a departure from high up in the branches, reaching the surface of the water and returning to the trees, where the birds eventually remain perched for a certain time before recommencing. I have observed on more than one occasion a sequence of courtship in which the male, perched near the water surface, flew away from the female in a semicircle and readvanced

in level flight, slow and hesitantly, simultaneously uttering a very varied song, made up of whistles, gurgles and little bursts, that some compare to that of the starling *(Sturnus vulgaris)*, the dipper *(Cinclus cinclus)*, or the goldfinch *(Carduelis chloris)*. That slow, level flight, which appears indecisive and hesitant, is a typical display. The two partners, often singing, fly to within a short distance of the water surface and almost always adopt circular trajectories. The courtship flights and calls can continue for hours at various times of the day, but are more frequent during the preliminary phase, while becoming less persistent between the first and second broods. The rapport between the partners can also include the "head-up" posture, which is very similar to the aggressive "upright-threat", but more relaxed and less aggressive, at least according to our interpretation. This preliminary phase to the definite formation of the pair usually involves only two birds, but five or seven have been observed together for a brief period of time. Such cases usually occur when there is a surplus population, with possible cases of polygamy that can be provoked as we have seen, by the modification of the parental roles. From various observations, the usual arrangement involves one male with two females, but it can also happen that a male has three mates.

At Saratov in the former Soviet Union, of 53 monitored nests, there were 42 monogamous pairs, 10 polygamous with two females and one with three. In this last case the burden on the male was very heavy especially if each female had two broods, there being ultimately six broods to look after. Observations made in other countries have also confirmed the possibility of polygamous unions. In Sweden, out of 116 nests, seven involved a male with two females, and in other regions of the former Soviet Union, in the reserve of Oka, 35 per cent of nests each year involved polygamous couples. As I have said above, these situations are sometimes provoked by the modification of the roles, given that the two females can brood simultaneously, or the male can pair with another female while the first is brooding. In the last case, for example, only the nestlings of the first brood need to be fed. Overlapping broods also occur in monogamous pairs, as we shall see later.

Fidelity to nesting site is very marked and each pair will use the same bank as the previous year and the same tunnels for nesting. The territory can change if one member of the pair dies or if, as often happens, the bank of the river crumbles or is altered in some way.

As I have already said in the chapter on Habitat, when there are no suitable sites near water, the nest can also be sited as far as several hundreds of metres inland (in Russia there are recorded distances of up to 2 km from the water). An essential consideration is that the walls in which the nesting tunnel is dug should be inaccessible to mammalian predators, in particular mustelids like the weasel *(Mustela nivalis)*. Observations made in Sweden, for example, have indicated that the fox *(Vulpes vulpes)* and the mink *(Mustela vison)*, are the most dangerous predators. In order to be suitable, the bank should be sufficiently high and vertical and should not offer footholds which predators could use either for climbing up to or descending down to the tunnel entrance. Moreover, the layer of earth above needs to be sufficiently deep.

I remember that in the "Bosco Negri", near Pavia, due to the absence of suitable banks near water, two pairs of kingfishers nested in the sandy walls formed by two big poplars uprooted by the wind. The sand which was held by the roots formed two enormous and practically vertical blocks more than three metres high. The distance apart was about 280 metres and the two pairs had a series of suitable holes for nesting. The kingfishers almost always returned from the water course, a distance of about 200 metres, from on high, flying over a tract of wood and descending almost vertically into the open space where the two trees had fallen, in such a way to avoid the intricacies of the vegetation. It is interesting that the kingfisher has this ability to choose suitable banks, taking account of the various necessary characteristics, even during its first breeding season.

I have watched the excavation of the nesting tunnel several times. Almost invariably the male starts the work, but subsequently it is divided equally between the two partners.

This bird's bill, dirty with earth, is evidence that the excavation of the nest has begun

During the courtship period the male (on the right) offers fish to the female in order to reinforce the pair bond. The fish are offered headfirst so that the female can swallow them easily

The male indicates the chosen point to the female, flying against the wall and striking it at first with his bill. Not yet able to gain a foothold on the surface, he keeps his balance with several wingbeats and after a few seconds, returns to the perch. The two partners usually sit not more than a metre from each other and they alternate in the work: one of the pair leaps from the branch, gives several blows and returns, the other then completes the same operation and so it continues until the excavation is large enough to permit the two birds to work side by side.

The bills are used for digging, while the feet rapidly eject the earth, which accumulates at the base of the bank. The two birds, working in turn inside the tunnel, make their plumage dirty with earth and on emerging, before perching on the branch, they dive frequently into water. Naturally, the time required to finish the work depends on the consistency of the earth and can last from four to about 13 days. The excavation is horizontal or more often slightly inclined upwards with a slope of not more than 20°.

The dimensions are on average as follows: length 55cm (these are measurements extending from a minimum and maximum of about 23 to 135cm); diameter of the tunnel, 5 to 5.5cm; nesting chamber 16x17 cm with a height of 11cm. The entrance hole is normally found some 90 to 180cm above the level of the water and in extreme cases can be encountered from 35cm to 70m.

The second brood is usually raised in another nest, generally a short distance from the first, often a few metres, while the third clutch, in the few cases in which this has been established, is normally deposited in the first nest after it has been cleaned out. When an overlap occurs, the cleaning of the second nest or its construction from new is done while the first still contains nestlings. Moreover, from the moment that the female starts the second brood, the male is occupied with the sole care and feeding of the young in the first nest, helped only occasionally by his mate.

Previously I have mentioned the possibility of mammals reaching the nesting tunnel and in fact I have had two opportunities to witness this event. The first happened in a bank of the river Sesia, in Piedmont, when a rat (*Rattus norvegicus*) succeeded in climbing up to the entrance of the nest, gripping the small roots that hung down the bank. The rat entered the tunnel with difficulty, while the female was in the nest with the young born a few days earlier, and after a few seconds it came out quickly backwards, fell in the water and swam away. I cannot say with certainty what happened, but it probably received a peck on the nose.

The second happened in a gravel-pit near Pavia. I arrived too late: the male was flying back and forth making continuous alarm calls, while near the nesting site one could clearly see the footprints of a mustelid, which had climbed up to the entrance hole. At the base of the bank,

Copulation usually occurs near the nest, and the male's advances are not always accepted.
The male arrives in flight, hovers for a moment and then alights on the female

The male balances with his wings and gently grips the head of the female with his bill.
Copulation begins during the final phase of nest construction and finishes at the end of the egg-laying period

Below: the female runs along the narrow, slightly upward-sloping tunnel that leads to the final chamber. Depending on the consistency of the soil, the process of excavation can last anything from four to 14 days.

Left: the kingfisher clinging to the vertical bank has started the work of excavating the tunnel, which will end in the nesting chamber.

Below: seven eggs comprise the first brood of the year

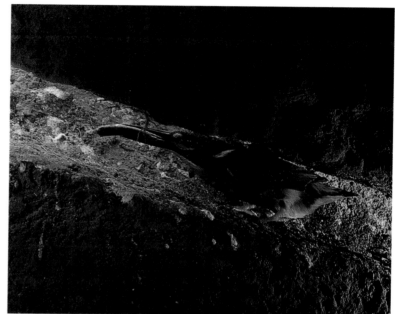

Above: this artificial nesting system in a riverbank was quickly occupied by a pair

*Above: the nestlings are born blind
and naked within a few hours of
each other, and do not open their
eyes until after the eighth day*

Above: the female takes the eggshells away from the nest

Left: while the female is in the nest with the young, the male arrives with food

Below and right: throughout the
first week, the parents take it in
turns to stay in the nest to brood
their young

Left: the nesting chamber with the nestlings

Above: The nestlings line up in a particular order for begging, and move round in such a way that each one receives food

Left: as the nestlings grow, the parent birds have to come out backwards from the tunnel as there is not enough room inside for them to turn round

some feathers and two broken eggs indicated that the predator, without doubt a weasel *(Mustela nivalis)*, had surprised the incubating female.

I should like to return now to the description of courtship, which I left at the point of food offerings. In courtship-feeding the male offers a fish to the female, holding it by the bill in such a way that she can swallow it headfirst.

This phase begins when the nesting tunnel is almost complete and is the first moment when the two birds come to make contact with their bills. As I was saying at the beginning of the chapter, aggression, or perhaps only a conditioned reflex, can be latent and the ceremony of the gift of fish can awaken postures similar to the aggressive attitudes. The male is sometimes reticent when offering fish to the female.

In such a case she solicits fervently and calls insistently at her mate perched beside her, even snatching the fish from his bill, as can be seen in the photograph on page 113. During the phase of courtship feeding the female often chases the male after he has captured a fish, inviting him with contact or begging calls to give her the prey. She remains perched beside her partner, with wings slightly open and trembling, neck elongated and tail barely uplifted. Such a display is almost identical to that of the young when they beg for food from their parents.

Often, when the female is perched, the male dives to catch a fish and returns to offer it to her, or after having caught it, he calls her with contact calls, inviting her to receive the gift further off. This is of precise significance in nesting success. The female needs to be sure of the competence of the male, as in the case of overlapping broods, he will need to feed the nestlings of the first brood and the female incubating the second, simultaneously.

The courtship ceremony, with the offering of fish to the female, occurs at various times during the day and continues until the start of incubation, then decreases rapidly. In this period the male feeds his mate about every 30 to 70 minutes, bringing the fish to the tunnel entrance or sometimes right into the nesting chamber.

Towards the final phase of the nest construction and during the period of egg-laying, mating occurs, often preceded by courtship feeding. Sometimes the female solicits the male, assuming an erect position and emitting a sibilant whistle, but often the male directly assumes the initiative, and is not always accepted. For as much as I have been able to observe, copulation takes place preferably in a separate place, but always near the nest and each time in a different place.

One of the parents arrives at the nest with prey

In order not to become abraded,
the feathers of the nestlings remain
inside a sheath of keratin and do
not emerge from the envelope until
a short while before fledging

As can be seen in the photographs on page 121, the male advances towards the female, remaining for an instant above her while hovering, then he alights onto the female's back, and she leans forward. During mating, the male balances with his wings and gently grips the neck or head of the female with the tip of his bill.

The ritual of copulation ends with the completion of the clutch, and is resumed for successive nests.

Throughout the period of time from incubating to hatching and then fledging of the nestlings, male and female alternate at the nest without particular ceremony. The bird on the outside advances, calling, and stops on a perch close to the nest site. The other comes out of the nest and flies away, generally responding to the call, while the first enters the tunnel. When it is preceded by a contact call, the changeover is very rapid, but at the beginning of incubation the two birds may not have yet established a rhythm and the female may emerge from the nest without the forewarning of the male.

Incubation lasts on average 19 to 21 days, with the parent birds alternating at the nest every 3 to 4 hours. The female usually sits in the morning and the male in the afternoon. The eggs, as can be seen clearly in the photograph on page 123, are white and almost spherical in shape. The dimensions are not always identical. Out of 100 eggs measured in England, for example, there were average dimensions of 22.67 x 18.63mm,

while similar measurements made in Belgium on a sample of 170 eggs furnished a result of 22.85 x 18.8mm. The maximum dimensions taken from various observations were 24.8 x 18.6 and 22.7 x 19.9mm, while the minimums were 20.9 x 18.4 and 23 x 16.7mm. Moreover, the number of eggs deposited in the first clutch is generally 6 to 7, more rarely 4, 5, 8 or 9, while the second and third clutches are on average more numerous.

As I have already said in a preceding chapter, it can happen that there is an excessive concentration of pairs in a limited space. This can occur, for example, when the birds that return to nesting sites after migration find the habitat changed by man. In this case, excessive closeness between the pairs can jeopardise nesting and some males may enter other nests in order to destroy the eggs. A similar, if rarer, event occurred in 1990 in an artificial nest which we located at the Bosco Negri, near to Pavia. Probably due to the cold and bad weather, the pair that had nested there had deposited only two eggs and we were concerned because of the presence of a second male near the nest. When the young were a few days old, Dr Bogliani, biologist of the University of Pavia, looked at the nest, and discovered that the two nestlings had been killed and had two holes in their breasts. The most likely theory is that the second male had killed the nestlings at a moment when both the parents were absent. The surprising thing was that the other nest was inside the wood, about 280 metres away, and therefore not excessively close.

A young kingfisher almost ready to take its first flight. The colour of the head is greener than that of the adults and the black bill has a white mark at the tip

Throughout the first week after the eggs hatch, the parents brood the nestlings, taking turns at intervals of a few hours. The nestlings are blind on hatching and their eyes open only after the eighth day. A few hours after hatching, the nestlings are fed with fish less than 4cm long and are capable of holding their heads up and of swallowing the fish.

During the period from hatching to fledging, some 23 to 27 days, the nestlings produce a repertoire of very diverse sounds that alter according to age. It is not possible to decipher and transcribe them all completely. There are nevertheless some characteristic calls that come to be repeated with much insistence, such as "vrhuii, vrhuii", or "rruu rrii", with which the nestlings from a few days of age solicit the parents to brood them. After the first 10 days the most characteristic call, audible at a distance of several metres from the nest is the food call: "uirr uirr". Then as age progresses, the various calls are not always easily interpreted, but at 17 to 18 days, an explosive "zipp", is emitted as a contact call and persists for about a week after fledging.

Inside the nesting chamber the nestlings assume from the first a particular configuration, with bills turned towards the light that indicates the entrance to the tunnel. Evidently, even if the eyes are still closed, they can perceive the light that penetrates from the outside. The parents, arriving at the nest, give the contact call and stop at the chamber entrance, proffering a fish held in such a position that the head points outwards from the tip of the bill. When the nearest nestling to the tunnel grasps the bill of the parent, it claims the fish, which is promptly released by the adult. The nestlings rotate their position in respect of the front of the tunnel, exactly like the bullets in the barrel of a pistol. The nestling in the position to be fed gives the food call incessantly until the parents arrive, then it is pushed aside by its siblings and stays silent until its next turn.

As the nestlings grow, their behaviour changes and after two or three weeks they assume Indian file, where each one almost overlaps the sibling standing in front of him.

From this moment they begin to compete, often breaking their regular turn and going along the tunnel to receive the food. In this phase, the nestlings assume "imploring" attitudes, with the wings slightly open and shivering, typical of the female during the courtship period.

I am often asked how the parents can be capable of locating the bill of the nestlings when they enter the tunnel from the light outside, as a motorist who drives into a very dark tunnel without putting on the lights cannot see. I consider that the white marks at the sides of the neck of the adults are two signals for the nestlings, enabling them to direct their bill towards the centre. The two marks, being illuminated in contralight, are without doubt visible within the tunnel.

The nest becomes very soiled from excrement of the nestlings which always eject towards the light, and from the accumulation of the food

Right and overleaf: fledglings, shortly after leaving the nest, waiting to be fed. The first flight is brief, and the birds usually alight on the nearest perch. The young kingfishers already begin to show a degree of aggression towards their fellow creatures. As is explained in this book, this behaviour is necessary to the survival of the species

pellets which are already present at the moment of brooding. These substances also produce a notable quantity of ammonia as Dr Baldaccini has discussed. The dirtiness of the nest probably soils the plumage of the adults, which dive often into water after having fed the nestlings. When the nestlings are big enough, the parents cease to enter the nest chamber, but remain in the tunnel from which they have to exit backwards, not having the space to turn round. The feathers of the nestlings are covered by a sheath of keratin which prevents them from becoming soiled. Only after the twentieth day, that is just before fledging, do the feathers emerge from their protective envelope.

When the young are nearly at the point of leaving the nest, the parents often enter the tunnel in silence and without food, or they give excitement calls from outside the tunnel. The first flight is brief as the young stop on a perch a small distance from the nest to await being fed. In a few days they disperse, chased by the adults, in different directions and to variable distances, from a few hundred metres to several kilometres. With the passing of days, the range of dispersion increases and some juveniles can infiltrate into spaces already occupied, where it is necessary to compete for feeding territory as we have seen in one of the preceding chapters. Thus their difficult and possibly brief adult life begins.

*One of the first dives of a young
kingfisher. At the end of the first
chapter of its life, the kingfisher
is able instinctively to capture
fish with precision, in spite of the
difference in the incidence of
light refraction between air and
water* *(see p. 106)*

PHOTOGRAPHY

*t*his last chapter is for those who want to know a little more about the subject of photography, and the photographs in this book. As I mentioned in the introduction, the photographs were taken in perfectly natural conditions, in various habitats frequented by kingfishers in north Italy. Most of the work was carried out in Veneto, at a property of mine, where I could work without disturbance. Because I had decided to record the kingfisher diving directly into the channel of the stream rather than into tanks containing fish, I had to solve some problems, such as the availability of prey at the ideal point of capture and at the right moment, the necessity of covering pools, and silencing the camera and flashes, etc. The camera, moreover, had to possess a very important feature: the delay from the moment of pressing the shutter button to the moment of exposure had to be as brief as possible. All cameras possess a "physiological" delay, determined by various mechanical operations like the raising of the mirror, the stop down of the diaphragm, the aperture of the shutter, etc. In practice, this means that the film does not show what is observed when the shutter is activated, but the action which comes fractionally afterwards. In order to record, for example, the moment at which the kingfisher crosses the water surface (photographed on page 43), I needed to be very certain that the mechanical delay was as brief as possible.

To obtain two successive images separated by only a few milliseconds, I used two identical Hasselblad camera bodies, linked and coupled together side by side. Naturally, in these cases the equipment was contained in a case placed at a suitable point, while the shutter was controlled in my hide by means of electric cable. For these "special" photos, I chose Hasselblad cameras, which, on a particular setting, reduced the delay to about three milliseconds against the average of 30 to 50 given by cameras with curtain shutters. On the few occasions when in similar circumstances I tried to use small format equipment, the results were often unsatisfactory. In some cases, only a portion of the bird's tail appeared in the photograph, or in some cases, it did not appear at all. The explanation is simple: a kingfisher in flight has a normal speed of about 6 to 8 metres a second, equivalent to about 25 to 30cm in 40 milliseconds, which, as I have said, represents the average shutter delay of a 35mm camera.

For the first photographs of the kingfisher under water, that I took more than 10 years ago, I used a cube of glass with sides of 40cm, with a plate of iron on the base for counteracting water pressure. The cube was located in a way that the open upperpart was level with the water surface. Inside, I placed the Hasselblad, the rechargeable batteries for the flashlights, etc. These were positioned on the outside, while one was left inside and to the front of the cube in order to soften the shadows. The camera was remote-controlled with an electric cable from the hide.

After I obtained my first satisfactory results, I then decided to try to capture in the same image the scene both above and below the water surface. The frontal lens of the wide angle Distagon 50 of the Hasselblad was leant against the glass of the cube, partly above, partly below the waterline. In this way I was able to photograph above and below the water level simultaneously, taking account of the different indices of refraction of air and water, which produced diverse effects in the two parts of the images. The part underwater was larger than that in air and so therefore the different depths of focus displaced one compared with another. It was therefore necessary to stop down the lens in order to have a greater depth of field, and this meant I had to use more powerful flashlighting.

Naturally, these things were very much more difficult to put into practice than they seemed in theory, and one of the most irritating problems was the condensation that covered the glass of the cube under the surface line. This happened when the external temperature was warmer than that of the water, and for this reason I had initially to limit myself to photographing in winter. Notwithstanding all this, some of these old photographs were very successful and one in particular became very famous and was used for several advertising campaigns, including Kodak in Great Britain, Hasselblad, Telefunken in South Africa, etc. In spite of encumbrances and the problems of condensation, the glass cube resolved my early problems, but I did not want to be restricted to taking pictures in this way only in winter. The next step was, therefore, to construct an underwater perspex housing for the Hasselblad, armed with connections to take the leads of the flashlamps, the release cable, etc. The special connectors were also completely silent and permitted vision through the lens of the camera. In this way I solved the problem of condensation and was able to continue photography throughout the year.

My hide at "Zelata" in the Ticino Park where my most recent photos and observations were made

At this point, my photographs began to appear in various European and international magazines, and some birdlovers, including Angelo Miramonti, began to photograph kingfishers with similar systems. With regard to more normal photographs taken out of water, in addition to the Hasselblad I have used small format cameras with various lenses, varying from a wide angle to an 800mm telephoto lens. Whenever possible, I have preferred to rely on natural light, while with the flash, I have tried to imitate natural light as faithfully as possible.

ACKNOWLEDGEMENTS

The author would like to thank the following people for their help in preparing this book. Professor Giuseppe Bogliani, Professor Carlo Violani, Dr. Marco Ferrari, Bruno Valenti, Pier Mario Nazari, Angelo Miramonti, Angelo Opezzo and Gunter Ziesler.
The following kindly supplied additional photographs: Angelo Miramonti (pp. 123-128, 132, 133), Angelo Opezzo (pp. 121, 135, 137), and Gunter Ziesler (pp. 12, 13, 15).

BIBLIOGRAPHY

The Living Bird, 1980, vol. 18

CRAMP, S. 1985. *The Birds of the Western Palaearctic;* [Vol.IV], Oxford University Press, Oxford

GLUTZ VON BLOTZHEIM, U.N. & BAUER, K.M. 1980. *Handbuch der Vögel Mitteleuropas,* [Vol. IX], Akademische Verlagsgesellschaft, Wiesbaden

HALLET, C. 1977. 'Contribution a l'étude du regime alimentaire du Martin pêcheur *(Alcedo atthis)* dans la vallée de la Lesse",*(Aves* 14) pp. 128-144.

HALLET, C. 1982. "Étude du comportement de prédation odu Martin pêcheur *(Alcedo atthis)* (L.): taille préférentielle de capture du chabot *(Cottus gobio)* et de la truite *(Salmo trutta)"; (Rev. Ecol.* 36), pp. 211-222.

BOAG, D. 1982, *The Kingfisher,* Blandford Press, Dorset.

LASKE, V.& HELBIG, A.J. "The winter resistence of a population of the European Kingfisher *(Alcedo atthis ispida)"*. in: FARINA A. (ed.) 1986, "First conference on birds wintering in the Mediterranean region". (*Suppl. Ric. Biol. Selvaggina,* vol. X).

BOGLIANI, G. & MASSARA, M. 1990. "Optimal Prey size for chicks of two species of single-prey loaders" (*Ethology and Ecology of Evolution,* 2) p. 299

BURTON, R. 1990. *Bird Flight,* Eddison Sadd Editions, London.